Construction Management:

DOCUMENT
TO REDUCE RISK

Dedication

My grandmother, Andrea Arcia Monzón, was a very educated, highly disciplined person of unwavering character and impeccable morals. Born in 1900, she studied at the University of Havana (as an adult student after her husband died prematurely), and became an English professor. Having lived with her in the same household while growing up in Cuba, then later in South Florida after my family emigrated, she cultivated my thirst for knowledge at an early age. Nearly all my memories of my grandmother involve teaching, reading, or learning something new. She taught me by example that, through discipline and steadfast application, I too could hope to acquire the wisdom that she possessed in her later years.

For as long as I can remember, I have been driven by the desire to learn and to acquire knowledge of things; all things. The intrinsic satisfaction that I get from learning something new, after putting in the effort and dedication that is required to learn, has been a constant source of joy in my life. Another source of joy is that which comes from sharing what I have learned, whether it be with my clients or my grandchildren. Sharing what I know with others is deeply gratifying.

I hope that you are as fortunate as I have been to have had someone in your life kindle that desire for knowledge within you. I have my grandmother to thank for enriching my life. This is the reason why I chose to dedicate this book to her memory.

Paco Farach
May 22, 2014

Construction Management:

DOCUMENT
TO REDUCE RISK

How to be a "PPRICK"

Without being a PRICK

A manual for project management

(Including sample letters)

Francisco "Paco" Farach

Construction Management:
Document to Reduce Risk

ISBN: 9781633180727

For more information, contact:
Francisco J. "Paco" Farach
11390 Lake Shore Drive
Cooper City, Florida 33026
pfarach@gmail.com

NOTICE TO THE READER

This manual contains suggested sample letters for use in managing construction projects. These letters serve as practical examples to assist managers in documenting the events and issues that typically arise during the construction process. Some communications such as reservation of rights, payment disputes, and positions on claims may be critical and should be considered carefully. The user is strongly encouraged to solicit the advice of a competent attorney prior to issuing critical communications.

Preface

During my thirty five years of experience as a subcontractor and consultant I have observed that the great majority of people who are responsible for managing construction projects are deficient in one or both of the following skills:

- Having a good working knowledge of the construction contract and understanding how it should be used to manage a project, and

- Preparing effective, timely correspondence regarding project issues

I have attempted to address both of these deficiencies in this manual. I have also tried to make the manual easy to read and use for all project participants, regardless of their current level of writing skill, formal education, or their familiarity with contract language.

This manual evolved from the seminars I have presented to contractors on documentation and avoiding claims. Each time I finished a presentation, I realized that it simply was not possible for me to cover all of the material that was necessary and answer all of the questions asked within the few hours that I had available. It also wasn't practical for contractors to make their key project personnel available for longer periods of time.

The material covered in this manual is therefore an expanded version of my seminar. I am able to go into greater detail and provide more advice and examples here than I could hope to include in a short seminar presentation.

The information presented here will benefit anyone involved in the management of construction projects from field representatives (foremen through superintendents) to office management and administrative staff (project managers through owners). Some readers may find that parts of this manual will serve to refresh what they already know. However, even the more skilled project participants should find something of value in the pages that follow.

How to Use This Manual

Being familiar with construction, you know that all specialized tools come with instructions provided to teach you the best way to use that tool. This manual is no different; it is a tool for construction management. To help you acquire and put to use the knowledge that resides within this manual, I have prepared suggested instructions for you on its use.

While you might be able to read this book from start to finish and learn the principles and concepts that I present, I believe you will get more lasting benefits if you approach the task in one of the ways I outline below, depending on your particular circumstance.

Owner, Executive or Sr. Manager:

There are several ways for you to benefit from this manual. Initially, I suggest you read through the material and review the sample letters included in Appendix B to become familiar with the examples provided.

Once you have understood the philosophy behind my approach to managing and documenting the project events from a contractual, "rules-based" perspective, you will be armed with the knowledge that will allow you to supervise the work of your subordinates to ensure they are managing their projects with risk reduction in mind.

I hope you will make it a point to incorporate the Contract "Rules" Checklist in your procedure for reviewing contracts and make sure it is used by everyone involved in any aspect of the work. By doing so, you, and your entire project team will have handy all the information that is critical to making important project decisions. This action alone could be the single most important step you take toward risk reduction on your projects.

You will want to keep the manual handy as a reference when you need to prepare correspondence concerning any of the numerous issues for which I provide examples for your use.

Project Manager:

You should consider treating this manual like a workbook. Read it through first to gain a general understanding. Then go back and study those areas where you may have found my approach or advice difficult to practice.

Keep the manual with you for reference and to provide you with a framework for making decisions and documenting the events that take place during the life of your construction projects.

Use the Contract "Rules" Checklist in Appendix A as your guide of the key contract clauses which require specific action by you when events arise that may expose your company to greater or new risks.

Take advantage of the sample letters included in Appendix B to kick start your correspondence on issues that need to be documented.

Finally, you may need to re-visit the guidelines I provide for effective writing in chapters 7 and 8 in order to continue to improve upon your skills.

Superintendent, Foremen:

The construction industry is one where many owners and executives of businesses first started their career as field supervisors. If that is your aspiration, then it is essential that you acquire the knowledge you will need to reach your goals.

In addition to learning about technical or trade-specific material, you will need to understand much more about the business risks that exist in construction. That includes knowledge of contracts and the conditions (or "rules") that come from them which end up dictating when, how, and why you must perform certain tasks when events take place in the field during the execution of the work.

As you read this manual, you should be seeking to understand the reasons why it is critical for you to report certain information regarding events in the field and to make sure that your superiors are made aware of those issues that could lead to greater risk as soon as possible.

One of the goals you should have if you are aiming for promotion to a management position in your company (or to run your own construction business someday), is to change your way of thinking about your work. You must begin to see how the work you do as a foreman or superintendent fits within the overall company. You need to develop your decision-making process to include consideration of the impacts that your actions in the field could have on the risks and rewards for your company. The more you think in business terms, the more value you will have to your company, no matter what position you hold today.

Contents

Contents

Introduction

You were just informed that you were the successful bidder on a recent bid. The scene in your office is probably one of celebration, congratulations, high fives all around, even drinks during "happy hour" after work.

But let me ask you, how many of the following questions can you answer "yes" to without hesitation?

- Do I know and understand the terms of the contract which I will be asked to sign?
- Do I know the general conditions, special conditions and other documents that will be incorporated into the contract?
- Do I even have a copy of them to review?
- Did I review the schedule for construction and does it include my work activities? Is the schedule realistic?
- Do I know how the requisition process will work and when I will get paid?
- Do I know how changes to my scope need to be handled?
- Do I know what costs I will be able to recover for changes in scope?
- Do I know what could happen if my customer does not agree with my price for extra work?
- Do I know what is expected of me if the project is delayed through my fault?
- Do I know if I can expect to recover any of my additional costs in the event the project is delayed through no fault of mine?
- Do I know …

At this point you might be saying, what the heck, why are you trying to spoil my celebration by asking about these details? Don't you understand the nature of the construction business? These details are all worked out later. I will know all of this by the time the contract is signed.

A few weeks later, when it's time to execute the final contract (probably after having mobilized the work in the field), you rush through, flipping the pages, overwhelmed by all the fine print and the legal-ease that you really don't want to spend the time reading and don't fully comprehend. You comfort yourself with the relief you feel having secured another chunk of work to keep your company afloat and your key employees working. You may even have a sense of pride for your accomplishment, having beat your competition once again. So you sign the contract!

Like most contractors, you probably had someone check the Scope of Work section of the contract to make sure that it matched your bid scope and glanced at the schedule to make sure it looked okay. If you're lucky you may have been able to review the estimate and even confirmed your main material quotes and subcontracts to make sure there would be no "surprises".

So, what's the big deal? You're ready to go to work, let's get the job going so you can submit your first draw and get some of that **new cash flow** into the company, you have payrolls to meet and bills to pay. Your thinking may even shift to what you will be able to do with the profit that you figured to make from this job.

Well, "IF" you're lucky, and "IF" things go right, you may not need to know the details of the contract you signed for a while. Heck, if you are one of the very rare ones, you may finish the job and get paid in full without ever having to know.

Okay, it's time for you to wake up now!

Let's face it, the odds of this happening these days are almost as good winning the lottery. My extensive experience tells me that it is almost certain that you will face numerous problems, conflicts, delays and disagreements on any given project, most of which will erode the bottom line profit that you figured to make. In fact, most projects will have many serious issues arise, forcing you to dig deep into that contract you rushed to sign (or have others do it for you at great expense).

Anyone who has been in this industry long enough would admit that there are a limited number of ways you can make money on a construction project, but there seem to be infinite possibilities to

2

lose money; and a lot of money at that, enough to take your company down!

The types of problems in construction projects are wide-ranging, but most common among them are:

a) defective plans and specifications
b) design changes
c) scope disputes
d) field conflicts between trades
e) interference by other trades
f) labor productivity issues
g) re-sequencing of work
h) schedule delays
i) schedule acceleration
j) payment delays
k) lack of payment
l) bad weather
m) submittal rejections
...and the list goes on.

It doesn't have to be that way though, with the proper approach, and the disciplined application of the right principles, you can navigate through any problem that may come your way to emerge successful upon completion of your projects.

Let me try to help you think about the role of project management in a different way. I believe that the primary goal of project management in construction is to do everything possible to shift the risk/reward ratio in your favor. The better you can manage your risks, the more likely it is that you will succeed.

Have you ever stopped to ask "what really happens when a contractor undertakes to build a project at a fixed price with a tight budget, a demanding schedule and a tough contract?" In this manual, I share with you my objective and honest view of what really takes place during construction. I will also guide you through some of the tougher circumstances that you will face along the way. Before we go there, let me introduce you to my concept for project management and reducing risk.

> **If you learn how to be a "PPRICK", without being a PRICK**
> **you will increase your chances of success.**

I decided to capture my approach to managing project risks with this catchy acronym so that it would get your attention and be easy to remember. Hopefully, I haven't offended anyone.

You see, I learned long ago that it's common in this business to label anyone that attempts to document issues as a "prick". To be fair, that label may be appropriate in many cases, due to the confrontational and antagonistic manner in which people perceive that their correspondence should be composed. As a result, in order to avoid getting the reputation of being a "prick", many project participants chose not to document construction issues. That is most unfortunate. I'm going to show you that it doesn't have to be this way at all.

My version of a construction management **"PPRICK"** practices the following principles:

Perform
be Proactive
be Responsive
write to Inform
be Clear when communicating
Know your contract

In addition to employing these principles, it is essential to adopt a cooperative, non-confrontational, and professional approach that is made evident by your actions and in your communications.

In the first chapter, I will expand on these "PPRICK" principles in detail. In subsequent chapters, I will visit typical situations that arise during the various stages of a project and suggest questions you should ask based on the type of frequently-encountered problems that may require documentation. My emphasis will be on the contract provisions that require you to document events at specific times when they occur. I demonstrate how these contract requirements can be viewed as the "rules" for project management.

I will emphasize the "PPRICK" principles that should be employed to help reduce risk along the way.

In later sections of the manual I will lay out what I consider to be the keys to effective writing for use in project management. Examples are provided for illustration using common problems and situations that should be familiar to you. My rules for writing are easy to understand and apply to the kind of effective writing that is necessary in this business. They are not the boring academic rules you would find in a typical grammar or composition book. I have developed my approach to writing after reflecting on the problems I have seen in correspondence I read over the years written by all levels of project personnel from field supervisors to owners and CEOs of large companies.

I have included two case studies in this manual for examples on how to document a problem from its origin to resolution. These are what I have found to be the most common problems: 1) extra work dispute; and 2) delay event that results in a request for additional time.

At the end of this manual you will find an appendix with my Contract Rules Checklist and another that contains sample paragraphs for many of the situations and problems that take place on most projects. These sample paragraphs can be used to guide you in creating your own document or as a template from which to customize your correspondence for your particular problem or issue.

My approach to this subject is practical, not theoretical. It is based on my personal experience having worked through these problems myself as a contractor or assisting others in an advisory role as their consultant. Having lived through the demanding experiences myself, I am motivated to help others prepare themselves to reduce the risks and increase the chance that their projects succeed.

This manual is not a legal guide for contractors; it is a tool for improving the skills you need to manage your projects. Though I talk about risks, liabilities and some contract terms in the process of educating you on the "PPRICK" principles I present, I do that in order to emphasize the reasons why certain actions are necessary in project management because they are good practices, based on the "rules" that are found in typical contracts. **You should not consider anything in this manual to be advice of a legal nature.** I believe that some of the best money you can spend as a contractor is in an up-front consultation with a competent attorney to help you review and negotiate your contract. Even if you have already signed a contract without the benefit of an attorney, it is essential that you get a complete understanding of your rights, duties and liabilities contained in the contract as soon as possible. Unless you are an experienced construction lawyer yourself, you need to get one to help you with this task. It need not be expensive if you prepare for it.

As you proceed through the contents of this manual I am sure many of you may find that what I am presenting will seem like common sense. However, what I have observed sadly throughout my career is that

> *Common sense is not common practice.*

I hope you will keep that in mind, and won't take this instruction for granted.

CHAPTER ONE

Manage Your Project Like a "PPRICK"

1.1 It's About Managing Risk

Many contractors I have known tend to view the construction market as a high risk / high reward casino where business fortunes can be made fairly fast by ordinary folks with the right skills, good people, hard work and the right connections. However, those contractors have a tendency to emphasize the "high reward" part and minimize the "high risk" part in their thinking (that's probably necessary in order to continue to operate in their environment).

After working in the construction business for a few years and seeing the enormous potential for risk, I realized that it was necessary to change the way I thought about a new project. I found it useful to think of a new project using the following definition:

> *New project: a liability for my company that remains on the balance sheet until the work is completed and collected for a profit.*

Where most contractors might use the occasion of being the successful bidder as a cause for celebration, I worried about the additional unknown liability exposure to which I had just committed my company.

Have you ever stopped to think about why it is that most construction contracts of any value require you to post a bond or some security backed by tangible assets as a pledge against your failure to perform? However, it is almost impossible to get anyone to value your company based on the potential profit that's reflected on an estimate at the beginning of a project? What does that tell you about the balance of risks to rewards in construction? A wise contractor knows deep down that there are more ways to lose money than there are to make money in construction – that's an unspoken truth.

One way of looking at the risk that unforeseen events may derail your performance during construction is to picture what it may look like over time. Below, I have constructed a graphic that I believe would be a fair approximation of what the level of risk may be during most construction projects as they approach completion. As you will see, during the majority of the time, those risks are high, decreasing slowly, until the project reaches its major milestones without significant delay or problems. Those milestones may be structural completion or building dry-in on some projects. On other projects that may not take place until interior framing and rough-ins have commenced. At that point, the majority of the construction has taken place and the job has been able to establish a flow that could take it through final completion pretty much on schedule.

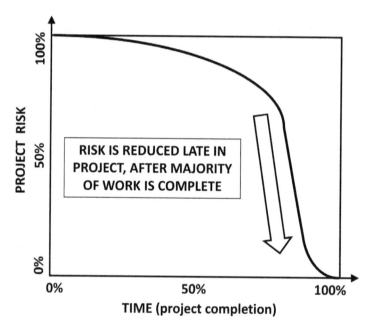

Some of you may see a parallel in this curve with the S-curve (inverted) that is typically used to represent progress in construction projects over time (although I have skewed the risk curve towards completion). Though the curve above may not hold true for all projects and circumstances, the point I am trying to make is that due to the inherent nature of the unknowns and the endless possibilities that exist for problems to occur during construction, there will be significant risks for contractors until the project is substantially complete.[1]

Unfortunately for contractors, their businesses are not subject to risk in just one dimension or those that affect only one resource. If that were the case, a contractor could hedge the risk of say prices rising for steel or copper by purchasing a futures contract to offset the increase over a specified time. That would limit the exposure that the contractor would have and reduce the risk. However, with the variety of materials, labor, equipment and other sources of input that a contractor has, it is not possible (nor economical) to begin to hedge all of the risks that are involved.

Contractors usually believe they have more control over the resources, events and conditions than they really have. So let's look objectively past those illusions to see which factors you have control over and which ones you don't.

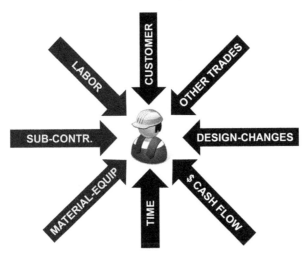

---

[1] Actually, it is possible to have project risk increase during the life of a project, since when adverse events take place they increase add to risk by definition. I am attempting to show only the risk that those events could take place during the course of construction.

❖ **Labor** – This is probably the largest budget item in construction. While you may have some degree of control over your labor force, it can be fickle, at times unpredictable, unreliable and even counter-productive.

Your labor costs are partly the product of internal company variables that affect the productivity of your labor force (e.g. hourly rate, benefits, training, experience, supervision, motivation, and other intangible factors). It is also subject to increases over time, and if your company employs union labor, it can be subject to additional factors over which you have little to no control (work slowdowns, stoppages, and strikes).

Finally, labor costs are also the result of the infinite problems and issues that arise during construction that affect conditions in the field (weather, equipment and materials availability, interference from other trades, poor contract documents, conflicting conditions, changes, delays, just to mention a few).

❖ **Subcontractors** – Whether you are a general contractor or subcontractor, you may contract with other companies to handle a portion or all of your work as a subcontractor to your company. As a natural consequence, you will lose a certain degree of control the minute you enter into agreement with another party through a contract. That loss of control will vary of course with factors such as their experience, available resources, quality of management, financial strength, your prior relationship with that company, leverage of other work, and other factors.

Even with the best subcontractors, you will always have to account for the additional response time that is required to direct their work and to implement new instructions or changes in the work. Since you are dealing with people, that response time will vary with the individuals involved, however, because you have to work through another layer of management, there will be a cost in time.

Whenever problems arise during construction, typically they are more difficult to resolve when you have to rely on a subcontractor due to that additional loss of control that exists by nature of the relationship. In the case of a lower quality subcontractor or where there exists a bad relationship with a subcontractor, the possibilities for the problem to be enlarged can increase greatly as well as the time and cost for resolving the problem.

Finally, as you know, many problems in construction arise from disagreement between the subcontractor and contractor over scope or conditions that are confined to the relationship between the subcontractor and contractor. These problems will most likely increase the risk of affecting the time and cost of your performance and you will be unable to pass that impact along to your customer. The best you can hope for is to pursue the additional costs and time with your subcontractor if the cause of the problem is ultimately determined not to be yours.

❖ **Suppliers / Materials** – Cost inflation, mistakes, theft, damage, shortages and manufacturing or shipping delays are many of the potential problems that can increase your cost and time of performance due to these project resources.

It is not always possible to fix the cost of all your material in the estimate with your suppliers in order to avoid the risk of cost inflation. Unfortunately, when price increases occur (which is fairly routine), they can be difficult if not impossible to pass on to your customer due to restrictions in your contract.

In addition, there are times when you discover a mistake in the price and/or quantity of some material component or quoted item which ends up taking more time and money to resolve.

It is also a fact of life that some portion of materials placed on a job site is bound to disappear through theft or rendered useless by damage or spoilage, both conditions potentially leading to delays and added cost. Even after materials are installed they are sometimes subject to vandalism on some projects. This not only forces you to reorder the material, but you will need to expend the labor again for its installation. Though you may have insurance coverage for these types of losses, you may choose not to file a claim due to a high deductible. Even if you do file a claim, you may not be able to recover in full for all of your loss.

The possibility always exists for shortages to develop in the supply chain, even for common materials. It also seems that no matter how diligent you are obtaining manufacturing commitments and shipping information ahead of time, there are also endless possibilities for delays due to factory problems, weather and other transit issues to cause critical materials to delay your work and increase your costs.

As it is impossible to predict or control any of these potential events, they must be viewed as additional risks which must be taken into consideration when bidding a project.

❖ **Equipment** – Some of the risks associated with this resource are similar to those for subcontractors (if the equipment is made available through a subcontractor) and materials described above (rental rate escalation, theft, damage, shortages).

In addition, equipment failure is a common problem which, though reduced through proper maintenance and use, will still take place at times with sudden disruption to your work. This will lead to additional time and cost of performance which cannot be controlled.

❖ **Time** – Considering the fact that most large projects provide for damages that will be assessed against you in the event you don't complete your work within the scheduled time, this is the most important resource. Unfortunately, time is a constantly diminishing resource that can never be increased.

Your only options to attempt to enlarge the time available for your work are to "accelerate" your performance through increasing your workforce or working overtime, including additional shifts. But even those efforts have their limits and they have associated impact costs and complications. In my experience the results of attempting to accelerate performance often fall short of expectations.

❖ **Finances / Cash Flow** – A factor that is central to all others, is your ability to finance your contracted work with your own source of funds. Whether you are a general contractor or a subcontractor, on most projects there will be times when you will need to supplement the cash flow of the project until you get payment for the next draw. This is necessary due to the very competitive nature of the construction business which is a low margin environment and has accepted payment practices that emphasize performance prior to payment.

Unless you receive substantial funds for mobilization or a large up front deposit on a project, you will consistently be performing ahead of payment with a percentage of your funds being held until the end (perhaps reduced at some point) which will leave you short of cash, even without the additional costs caused by problems during the job. This may be the situation for the entire duration of the project until you receive your final payment and retention.

Finally, on nearly all projects that develop serious problems because of disputed extra work or delays, you will need to be prepared to finance a larger portion of the work out of your own sources. On those projects with severe delays and other issues, you will need to spend even more of your resources in order to fund the struggle required by a lengthy dispute resolution process (arbitration or litigation) so that you may have a chance ultimately to recover a portion or all of your losses.

❖ **Design / Changes** – One of the most common risks in construction is that of the degree of completeness, accuracy and quality of the design for the project as represented in the Contract Documents. As a contractor bidding on a new project, it is not possible to perform a complete review of the design in order to determine how good the Contract Documents are. In addition, it is typical for owners to go to bid with only partially design documents with the goal of having the design "finalized" by the time the contract is awarded.

We know that in the real world the design for many projects are not finalized when the contracts are awarded. This often becomes the cause of many serious disputes that can plague a job throughout construction and cripple a contractor.

In addition, even on jobs where the design may be complete, there are usually changes to the design that arise either from owner or end user requests, code requirements or budgetary constraints. While many contractors may view changes as an opportunity to enhance their profit on a project, when all of the cost factors are accounted for and the limitations of the contract on pricing the changes are considered, I don't believe that changes are the wellspring of profits that contractors think they are.

Finally, let's not forget that in nearly all cases, work on changes will need to be financed as well; usually longer than anticipated. Whether the changes on a project add to the bottom line or not, we can agree that they are another of the unknown factors over which the contractor has no control.

❖ **Other Trades** – If you are a subcontractor, there are other trades that will affect your performance during construction. The impact of other trades on your work and profitability can be significant. Unfortunately you will probably have no direct control over the problems and issues that are caused by other trades. The most impact you may be able to exercise is that of influencing through your active participation at project meetings and through your correspondence.

There may be other prime contractors or trades working on portions of the same project that could affect your performance as well. Again, it is unlikely that you will have any direct control over the problems and issues caused by other prime contractors or trades.

❖ **Customer** – The final wild card in construction is that of the customer, who as we have learned, is "always right." What that translates to Is that many times the customer gets the final word on issues such as scope changes, extra costs, time, standards for acceptance, and other major project decisions. As a contractor, you are generally trying to please the customer at the expense of your bottom line. If the customer ends up being fickle, abusive, arbitrary or difficult, that will have an adverse effect on the profitability of your project. Unless you have had prior direct experience with the customer, you may be unable to gauge the risks associated with working for a new customer.

❖ **Other Risk Factors** - There are many other additional factors that come into play with the potential to increase your construction risk and add to your cost and time of performance. Among the most common ones (not listed above) are: weather and natural disasters, regulatory agencies, unforeseen conditions, and inspection authorities).

Once you understand the potential that exists for nearly endless sources of conflict and negative impacts caused by conditions outside of your control, it would appear to be a miracle that any project could be built on budget and on time. As a matter of fact, not many are.

1.2 How to Manage Like a "PPRICK"

As we saw in the prior section, being a contractor can be very risky and tough work. In addition to the variables I discussed above, here are some other reasons that come to mind:

- there is fierce competition
- you have less leverage
- it is a high risk/low profit market
- the environment is highly litigious

- performance is time sensitive (with stiff damages if late)
- the work environment is pressure-packed with conditions that are very fluid
- there is very little that is certain
- you are lower down the "food" chain

In light of the lack of control over our resources, the unknown factors that exist in construction, and the difficulties described above, it is clear that what is needed for managing construction projects is a way of thinking (an approach) that identifies and eliminates or reduces risks throughout every step of construction.

My approach to managing project risks has a catchy acronym to get your attention and make it easy to remember. A construction management "PPRICK" practices the six principles that make up my acronym.

HOW TO BE A "PPRICK"

Perform

be **P**roactive

be **R**esponsive

write to **I**nform

be **C**lear when communicating

Know your contract

Let me explain why I have selected these principles to be essential qualities for good project managers. I will start with the last one first:

❖ **Know your contract**: A working knowledge of the contract is the foundation from which all good project management decisions and actions should be based. The construction contract contains the "rules" that need to be followed when managing a project. Some of these rules may be stated clearly, others may be more subtle or require you to get help to interpret them.

If you do not know your contract, you will have no idea of the liabilities and damages to which you are exposed for your failure to perform. Likewise, you will not know how to go about reducing or eliminating the various risks that arise from issues and circumstances that develop during construction.

Lastly, you will not realize that your contract actually requires you to document conditions and problems in order to allow you to recover your extra costs and time of performance. Without knowledge of the contract, you will not know the necessary steps you must take to recover from the impact of those events or issues. In short, a working knowledge of your contract will act as a firm platform from which you can minimize your risks and maximize your profits.

[Chapter Two: Know Your Contract, and Chapter Three: Finding the "Rules" in the Contract, will expand more on this principle]

❖ **Perform**: There is no substitute for performance. By performing, you uphold your end of the bargain (as defined in your contract). You will eliminate the risks and the potential liability (damages) for the consequences of your failure to perform in accordance with the contract. From the point of view of minimizing your risks, by performing, you are closing the door on self-inflicted damages that you would invite through your poor performance. Throughout the entire construction process, your main focus should be on performance and on those conditions that will allow you to perform your work.

[Chapter Four: Perform, will expand more on this principle]

❖ **Proactive**: Proactive management is constantly looking ahead to spot any potential circumstance that may increase the risks on a project and is acting in ways to avoid or minimize the development of that circumstance. As a proactive project manager, you should be vigilant and defend against all events and conditions that threaten your company's ability to perform. You need to view all events on the project through an "early warning radar" that is tuned to detect any condition, event, or circumstance that may increase the cost or time it will take for your company to perform its scope of work.

You must follow the contract "rules" to document those additional potential risks that are spotted. If the events that bring higher risk are unavoidable, then the proactive manager in you will devise and implement a plan that best deals with the event, and to move through it to get past the risk as quickly as possible with minimal extra cost.

Finally, as a proactive manager, you are able to read the signs that allow you to predict events, rather than be surprised when the events unfold. Proactive management is "active", rather than "passive".

[Chapter Five: Be Proactive, will expand more on this principle]

❖ **Responsive**: As a responsive manager, you know that there can be damaging consequences for failing to act when a request, misrepresentation, or accusation is made. When you practice this type of management, you are aware of the significance of the written record of a project and see to it that the record reflects the facts.

Being a responsive manager, you know that the risks for your company can be reduced through the proper documentation of events during construction. As a responsive manager, you will also be aware of the damage that can be done through procrastination which can result in a failure to respond timely to issues and events in writing as required by the contract.

[Chapter Six: Be Responsive, will expand more on this principle]

❖ **Informing**: This is the first of two essential keys to effective writing for project managers. Construction is a complex effort that requires extensive and continued interaction between you and many different parties. Good communication is the key to efficient transmission of information. The better you convey that information, the faster and more efficient decisions can be made to continue to move the project.

The information that you need to communicate in construction correspondence is by nature heavily laden with facts. It is essential that you use a writing style that facilitates the flow of information, rather than one that interferes with discovery of information or relies on opinions instead.

[Chapter Seven: Write to Inform, will expand more on this principle]

❖ **Clear**: As with all good communication, your writing to document construction project issues should aim for clarity. I have come up with a list of six rules for writing that will help you achieve that goal. They are:

1. Don't try to impress with your writing
2. Stick to familiar words
3. Be direct
4. Don't be repetitive
5. Deal with one thought at a time
6. Avoid profanity, exaggeration, jokes, personal attacks, and similar pitfalls.

[Chapter Eight: Being Clear when Communicating, will expand more on this principle]

Throughout the next several chapters I will expand on these "PPRICK" principles and demonstrate how they can be employed in typical project situations to help you manage the project, minimize risk, and help you fulfill the responsibilities of your contract.

CHAPTER TWO

Know Your Contract

PPRIC<u>K</u>

2.1 The Contract "Gets no Respect"

When I first started in the construction industry, in 1978, there were some contractors that remembered building projects on a handshake and a select few that claimed they still did. Yes, that's right, no documents, no lawyers – life was simpler then. Of course, larger construction work was undertaken with the formalities of a written contract, but often that was a standard agreement and the terms were usually open for negotiation, even if you were a small contractor. For the most part, I remember that contracts tended to be much fairer as a whole.

As I progressed in the business, I found myself in the position of Vice President of Construction. One of my responsibilities in that role was that of reviewing contracts for my company and negotiating the terms and conditions. In addition, all important project issues were brought to my attention and I worked with the various project managers to guide them through the course of action that was best suited for each of the particular conditions. Even with all of the experience that I had acquired at that point, I realized that contractors (and subcontractors in particular) were at a great disadvantage when it came to the contract.

That was many years ago! Needless to say, contracts have become much more complicated since then and the construction business has become increasingly litigious.

In my cumulative experience in the industry (as a contractor and as a consultant working with contractors) I have made the following troubling observations:

- Some contractors don't read their contracts, they only check price and scope
- Few try to negotiate restrictive or unfair terms
- Many don't get all the documents that make up their contract
- Few contractors know how to use the contract to manage a construction project

While it is true that most of the time these observations apply to smaller contractors and subcontractors, I can tell you that is not always the case. I have been involved in several cases where "established", "reputable" companies have been guilty of some or all of the shortcomings described above.

Even in the case where the contract is reviewed in detail, often it's placed in a file drawer and not taken out again (usually forgotten)...until that point in time when the "stuff" has already hit the fan and it's time to call a lawyer.

This practice has led me to label the contract the "Rodney Dangerfield of construction documents!" It's a document that simply *"gets no respect."* So why is that the case? I could give you a long answer with all of the reasons I believe are true, but the short answer is this:

> *Contracts are written by lawyers – you're not supposed to understand them without familiarity with legal jargon and concepts.*

That being said, your reluctance to seek the help of an attorney to review the contract prior to execution is understandable. Contracts can be intimidating and a good attorney will command a hefty fee that may seem prohibitive. With razor-thin profit margins on most projects, every dollar saved is a dollar earned, or so you may think at the beginning of a project.

Yet, unless you are a contractor that has **never** had any serious problems on your jobs, you know from personal experience that when things go wrong during a construction project (which they almost always do) it is the language in the contract which dictates the "rules" that are applied to resolve the problems. This is especially true when serious issues arise during a project which threatens to increase significantly the cost or construction time. At that point, all verbal agreements, unwritten promises and other informal understandings will be erased from memories. Suddenly, the good will and that cooperative "team spirit" that you had enjoyed also seem to disappear. From that point on, every consideration, each decision and all actions will be strictly based on what was "agreed to" in the contract.

If you did not seek expert advice at the beginning, and started without a good working knowledge of the contract, you will probably rush to an attorney out of fear when immediate action is required after the problem has reared its ugly head. Making matters worse, due to your lack of understanding of the contract, you will need more time from your attorney at that point to guide you through the maze of contract clauses to choose the best course of action to take. Out of fear you may even decide to have your attorney draft all of your letters for you.

Finally, since you were not following the "rules" of the contract to provide the required timely notice of problems, preparing a record of communications in advance before the issue moved to "front burner" status, you will find that you're playing catch-up. Having failed to document properly in the past, you will be arguing the issue from a position of weakness. Unfortunately by then, you will already have spent more in legal fees than you expected, yet you may have only begun to scratch at the surface of the problem! Does this story sound familiar? I have seen it played out many times before.

In my opinion, it is the lack of understanding of the contract which causes many construction issues to be mishandled from the beginning. This is primarily a result of not knowing the specific requirements in the contract that address how you must communicate and record important issues; the kind of issues that typically lead to increased cost or time of performance on a project. In those cases when the issues are not documented according to the contract, the ultimate resolution of the problem will take longer and will be more costly than necessary. Usually, those issues won't get resolved until the end of the project and result in reduced profit (or a loss) on the project.

Regardless of your distaste for lawyers or your opinion that they are too costly, if there is one time during the entire life of the project when spending money on an attorney makes sense, it's the initial review of the contract before its execution!

2.2 What is a Contract?

This is not meant to be a trick question. I am often amazed, and at times amused with the answers I get when I pose this question to contractors. Their answers can be quite interesting and creative. They also are indicative of the variety of misconceptions that are at the root of the incorrect thinking that exists about contracts.

My definition attempts to boil things down to the bare essentials of what takes place when two parties enter into a contract. But before I share that with you I must offer my disclaimer: **THIS IS NOT A LEGAL DEFINITION AND I AM NOT A LAWYER!**

> *A construction contract is a legally binding exchange of promises between two parties in which one party promises to provide money in exchange (over a period of time) for a promise from the other party to perform a "scope of work" in accordance with rules that are established for that exchange.*

There, now I will give you my very basic and practical understanding of what takes place when you contract for work in construction.

The rules for that exchange of promises are what we don't pay enough attention to in my opinion. Misunderstandings and disagreements over the meaning and application of the rules is where most construction disputes originate and where construction lawyers (and consultants) make their living.

When you take a close look at the terms and conditions of the contract (what I call the "rules") you realize that the majority of them describe detailed requirements that must be performed for specific conditions or situations during construction. In fact, many of them set up threshold conditions which, if not met, would cause you to forfeit a right you might have in the contract.

For example, take the case of your right to have additional time to perform your contract in the event a delay takes place which was not caused by your company. One of the "rules" in the contract may say that you must notify the owner (or GC if you are a subcontractor) within 5 days of the commencement (or your awareness) of the delay. Your contract may state that failure to provide that notice will not entitle you to any extension of time at all. Unfair as that may be, that is what it says! This "rule" then establishes a duty on your part to document in writing and to communicate all events on the project that may delay the work, causing you to need additional time to perform your work. If you ignore the "rule" then you risk losing the ability to gain more time, and possibly subject your company to liquidated damages in the even the project is completed late.

In many cases the reaction to a notice of delay by contractors and owners is to act as if the need to document these events is optional and they get upset that a notice was sent to them. I have always pointed out in these situations that the contract is clear in making it an obligation to document the delay, just like there is an obligation to build the work in accordance with the plans and specs. My suggested response to any criticism about documentation is to state the fact that it is required by the contract and *"if you don't like it, then please modify the contract to get rid of that requirement so I won't have to document it."*

The point I am making here is very important and bears re-stating.

> *Once you understand the contract, you will see that there are specific requirements that cause you to document events and conditions, which if you don't, may increase your risk on the project and subject you to additional, unnecessary costs.*

I have given you only one example above. There are many other contract clauses that set up conditions which, if not followed, could result in your loss of certain key rights and increase your risk of performance.

When you begin to see the contract in these terms, you will change your way of thinking about the need for documentation. This will change the way you manage your projects in the future. You will no longer see it as doing something that is optional and objectionable, but instead, as a requirement that you are bound to do under the contract; a critical aspect of good project management.

Let me take the opportunity at this point to share some general observations that I have made about contracts which I believe are worth discussing. They might also help you reshape your concept of a contract.

1. **Contracts don't have to be fair** – In fact, most are not. The degree of unfairness of a contract at execution will typically be in proportion to the perceived relative bargaining power that the respective parties have in the deal.

   I have often heard arguments from contractors that they feel they are entitled to this or that because otherwise it would not be "fair". I always take them back to the contract that they signed and show them what they agreed to. So, if it was not fair then, guess what? They should have considered that when they were reviewing their contract (which is usually an indication that they did not review it).

   Another argument I have heard is that if the contract is unfair in this situation, then when they get to arbitration (or court) their argument will prevail because the contract was

26

unfair and the arbitrator (or judge) would make it fair. I would not take that side of the bet either if I were you!

My advice to you is simple; know what the contract says, have a lawyer explain the risks to you, and if you don't think it is fair, you must change it, not sign it, or live with the unfairness (and hope that you priced it accordingly).

Sometimes it Pays to Walk Away From the Contract

A long time ago, when I was working as a subcontractor, I was involved in a project that had gone bad. I had just finished attending a bitter mediation session in which I had settled my company's modest claims for delay and unpaid extra work.

My customer, the general contractor on the project, had not fared as well, having lost a significant sum of money despite years of hard work.

During the drive back to our offices (we had attended the mediation together) he was understandably upset over the outcome, yet relieved that his ordeal had ended. I took the opportunity to ask him what he could have done differently, now that he had the benefit of looking back.

Without hesitation, he stated "we should have walked away from the contract when we were in negotiations." He informed me that his company had spent over $50,000 in legal fees over several months in order to be able to execute the contract. That was in the early '80s!

He said that his customer (the developer) was a group of lawyers who were intent on crafting a deal which was as one-sided as possible. His company's desire to build the project had overshadowed the need to have a fair contract and a workable relationship with his customer.

"He should have just walked away!"

2. **Contracts don't have to be in writing** – It is true that there is nothing (other than common sense) that prevents you from entering into an oral agreement. But, knowing what you know about the construction environment, why would you want to do that? Think about it, if it is difficult to agree on the meaning of the written word, how much harder will it be to know what the meaning is when the words were spoken and subject to different memories? I have heard lawyers argue in disputes that the written contract was modified by oral agreement, even in cases where the contract states that no modification is valid unless in writing. Those make for interesting arguments to say the least! A word to the wise; play it safe, follow the rules in your contract and get your modifications, changes, directives and all instructions on critical issues in writing *before* you proceed with the work! After all, that is what your contract likely requires.

3. **You don't have to be a lawyer to prepare your own contract** – Yes, this is true and contractors used to do this long ago. However, with the substantial risks that exist in construction it doesn't make sense to try to enter into a contract of a significant size without legal assistance, especially when the other side has a lawyer working on their behalf. Why enter into the deal at a disadvantage? Don't you want to try to get the best terms possible?

4. **Contracts don't have to be easy to understand** – How true! I have been involved on projects where the contract was so convoluted and poorly written that even the lawyers could not decipher the meaning of key clauses. In my experience, those contracts are usually ones in which different lawyers have made numerous revisions over time, adding and deleting language, without making the effort to see if it made sense in light of other existing language. I should also point out that, yes, even among lawyers, one is bound to find some that simply don't have good writing skills.

5. **Just because something was written in a contract does not make it legal** – In addition to the problem of fairness we discussed above, there are clauses in some contracts that

are unenforceable. This is has nothing to do with fairness, but instead, is the result of laws that have been passed which make such clauses illegal. Contracts will typically contain a provision stating that if there are any such clauses in the contract the remainder of the contract clauses will not be invalidated.

So far I have given you reasons why it is in your best interest to seek the help of an attorney to review and understand the contracts that you sign. Now let me share with you what I recommend you should do when you meet with your attorney.

2.3 *Review the Contract with Your Attorney*

Ideally, you should have that meeting with your attorney **before** executing the contract. If at all possible, your attorney should point out those clauses that you should try to negotiate and the suggested changes to the language that would make them better.

I used to prepare for my meeting with the lawyer by reviewing the contract first and making two lists; one of the clauses that I found objectionable, the other of those that I had a problem understanding, or had questions about. I would also make sure to send a copy of the contract to my attorney prior to my meeting, with a request that he review it before our meeting. Having a good familiarity with the general arrangement and content of the contract, my meeting with the attorney was more productive.

My goals for the meeting were to get a thorough understanding of the contract, to identify the more problematic clauses for my company and come up with suggested changes for negotiation. A practical rule of thumb that worked for me was to come up with a list of proposed changes to the contract to submit for consideration, but to identify as a top priority for myself the three most important clauses that needed to be changed. Those three clauses were the ones which I would be prepared to fight for until the end. I was willing to sacrifice the other proposed changes when negotiating the contract, if necessary, to get agreement on my top three revisions.

If at all possible, you should have your lawyer draft the proposed language for the clauses that need to be negotiated during your meeting. When you leave the meeting, you should have a document that you can submit for consideration to the other side in your negotiation of the contract. Depending on the circumstances (e.g. size of the project, difficulty anticipated in negotiation) you may want to have your lawyer involved in the actual negotiation of the language with his counterpart on the other side.

By the way, in this pre-construction meeting with your lawyer, it is not necessary to meet with any other junior lawyers or paralegals – the interpretation of the proposed contract language is something your lawyer should be able to provide you from his knowledge and experience. You should not need to pay for additional legal support staff to attend this meeting. If your lawyer insists on having other personnel present you should consider hiring a different lawyer.

If circumstances did not allow you to review the contract with your lawyer before execution, then you will have foregone the benefit of sound legal advice prior to entering into the deal. That could turn out to be a grave error. Nevertheless, even if your meeting takes place after you have executed the contract, many of the benefits of meeting with your attorney remain: getting a thorough understanding of the contract, identifying the risks, potential liabilities, and the obligations that you undertook when you signed the contract.

Many of the standard contract clauses are considered "boiler-plate" and your lawyer will be very familiar with them, having seen them many times before. There will also be large sections of the contract that will pertain to safety, regulatory requirements, drawing lists, schedules, accounting, and other matters for which it does not make sense (or produce any benefit) to have your lawyer review. The same holds true for the specific job performance clauses that are particular to your scope of work or to technical aspects of your bid. You are best served having your staff review these to confirm and become familiar with them.

If you follow my advice and prepare for your initial meeting with your lawyer, the meeting should not take a long time and should not be so expensive.

Finally, I urge you to take advantage of your meeting with the attorney to help you find the "rules" for project management that reside in the contract. In the next chapter I will introduce the Contract Rules Checklist that you should use in your meeting with your lawyer.

CHAPTER THREE

Finding the "Rules" in the Contract

One of the objectives of this manual is to get you to think about managing construction projects in terms of applying the "rules" that are contained in the contract. Most of the rules discussed are found by a plain reading of the contract and refer to practical requirements that are clearly stated in most contracts (e.g. number of days to give notice, contract time, change order mark-up, or procedure for pricing and submitting changes). Other requirements can be more subtle and more difficult to interpret (e.g. damages for delay, extension of time).

As a project manager, you should get to know your contract inside and out before any problems or situations present themselves. In my opinion, the best money ever spent with an attorney is in a meeting at the beginning of a project in order to gain a good understanding of all the terms and conditions of the contract as they apply to the execution of the work and the management and resolution of problems that arise during construction. That way, armed with the knowledge of the contract beforehand, when a problem arrives you will be able to make informed decisions quickly and confidently, without the need for outside consultation or delay.

3.1 Contract "Rules" Checklist

The rules in the contract are there for a variety of reasons. Among them are:

- Enforce the design - Some rules are there to ensure contractors build what was designed in accordance with the Construction Documents. Examples of these are notice of non-conformance, corrective work requirements, and the deductive change clause to compensate for corrective work done by others.

33

- Adherence to the schedule – Clauses in the contract dealing with acceleration, supplementation of forces, and liquidated damages are some of the rules that can be enforced to attempt to keep the work on schedule.

- Fairness – The requirement for a contractor to give notice to advise the owner of extra work that will result in increased cost or additional time fits this category. This type of rule allows the owner to make an informed decision on whether or not to proceed with the change, or to modify the nature of the change to reduce its impact.

- Control the work area or to provide a controlled environment – There are contract clauses that specify access restrictions, clean up, attendance at meetings, and hours of work. These are some of the rules placed in the contract to give control over the job site and the environment.

Regardless of the reasons for the existence of these rules, our actions and the decisions that we make when managing projects must take into consideration and be in compliance with the rules of the contract or we assume added risk and suffer the consequences.

Over the years I developed a tool to remind me of the pertinent terms and conditions of the contract (the "rules") and their location within the contract for quick reference. This tool is a worksheet that lists the typical subjects within each of the stages of a project with columns for you to enter the contract clauses that pertain to the subject areas, the notice requirements and other comments you may want to note from your review of the contract.

Below is what a portion of the form looks like (a full version is included in Appendix A). As an owner of this manual, you can download a copy of this form (in Microsoft Word file format) from my resource website at **www.constructionletters.com**.

Contract "Rules" Checklist

Project: _____   by: _____

Project Stage & Subject	Clauses in Contract	Clauses in Other Docs.	Written Notice?	Days to Notify	Who Gives Authority?	Notes / Comments
PAYMENT						
Payments (progress)						
Stored Materials						
Retainage						
Non-Payment						
Interest on Payment						
CHANGES						
Change Orders						
Cost & Pricing Changes						
Differing (concealed) Conditions						
Change Directives						
TIME, SCHEDULE, DELAY						
Time (completion)						
Progress Schedules						
Interference & Obstructions						
Time Extension						
Acceleration						
Suspension of Work						

You should complete as much of this form as you can in your initial review of the contract and bring the form to the meeting with your lawyer to note comments about important clauses to make sure that you have understood the rules correctly from your initial review.

The form has several uses and benefits. It serves as a useful, ready index of the most often used contract rules, organized in a way that makes sense when managing a project. When completed correctly, I have found the form to provide the answers to my contract questions quickly, usually without the need to refer to the actual contract document. Since I had many projects simultaneously under my responsibility when I worked as a contractor, this form was my first point of reference when I picked up a contract file (in fact, I made sure my assistant had this form at the top of every contract folder).

Another benefit of this form is that of educating the project participants on your team that need contract information for various purposes. The completed form should be shared throughout the company to provide others with the specific rules from the contract that apply to their area of concern.

Occasionally, I provided the form to my attorney in the past for his quick familiarization of a contract when I needed to engage his services to assist in difficult issues on projects.

3.2 Questions to Ask While Reviewing the Contract

In order to provide you with a better insight into how to review your contracts I have prepared a list of questions that I use whenever I go through the key sections of a contract. This list may not include every question that could be asked, but it should give you a good start and have you approach this important task in the right frame of mind.

Topic: Getting Paid

- Is payment under the contract pay **_when_** paid, or pay **_if_** paid?
- When is the application for payment due?
- Through what period does the payment application cover?
- To whom is the payment application sent?
- What supporting documents must be included with the payment application?
- When is the payment due for monthly applications?

Topic: Changes and Extra Work

- When must a request for additional compensation or time due to an event or condition be submitted?
- In what form must it be made?
- To whom must the request be submitted?
- Is there a specified method for pricing the additional cost?
- Are there unit prices to be used for extra work?
- What support must be provided with the request?
- Is extra work authorized by written Change Order?
- Can extra work proceed without written approval?
- What could happen if extra work is started without approval of the change?
- How are changes for extra work submitted for payment?
- When is payment for changes due?

Topic: Disputed Changes and Extra Work

- What happens when there is agreement on entitlement for the change, but not on the cost or time requested?
  - Is there a written directive to proceed with the work and a specified way to bill for it? (cost plus a markup?)

- If so, what costs qualify to be included in billing?
- What records must be kept and submitted to support the bills?

- Who is the final authority to determine the outcome of a change request when there is no agreement on the cost or time? (The Architect? The Contractor?)
- What happens when there is no agreement on entitlement for the change? Can I still be forced to perform the work?
- If a change order request is rejected without merit and I am forced to proceed with a written directive or forced work order how can I object? Is there a time requirement to object?
- Do I need to submit a notice of claim for a disputed change?
- Is there a time frame within which I must submit? Do I lose my right to submit if I don't provide my notice on time?
- How, to whom, and where are my claims to be filed and resolved?

Topic: Construction Time and Schedule
- What is the time allowed for construction from the start to substantial completion?
- What determines the start of the contract time? (NOC? NTP?)
- Is "time is of the essence" a condition in the contract?
- Who creates, updates and manages the schedule?
- Am I required to submit a schedule of my work activities?
- How is the float in the schedule to be used?

Topic: Coordination & Sequence
- Who is responsible for overall coordination of the project?
- What is required for coordination (drawings, submissions, attendance at periodic meetings)?
- If there are periodic meetings, are they mandatory? Are there penalties for not attending the meetings?
- Can work be re-sequenced without extra compensation?
- If so, under what conditions?

Topic: Delays / Overtime & Acceleration
- What does the contract say about recovering from delays?
- Can I be forced to accelerate my work? How? (By written notice? Directive? Change Order?)
- Can I get paid for acceleration if the delay was not my fault?
- Is a recovery schedule required? Who prepares it?
- For delays caused by others is an extension of time the only remedy?
- What is the notice requirement for delay?
- How often do I need to provide notice of delay?
- What costs are recoverable for acceleration?
- What records do I need to maintain?

Topic: Liquidated Damages
- Are there "liquidated damages" for delay?
- If so, how much are they?
- When do liquidated damages start?
- How are they calculated?
- Is there a grace period?

Topic: Claims & Disputes
- Can I make a claim for disputed changes or delays?
- What is the notice requirement?
- To whom must the claim be submitted?
- Does the Architect need to rule on the claim before it can proceed to a higher authority?
- Is there a time period for the Architect to respond to my claim?

Topic: Resolution of Disputes
- If I am not satisfied with the final decision of the Architect, GC, or Owner what can I do?
- Is there a time period for me to respond to the decision of the Architect or Owner?
- Do I need to demand mediation, arbitration, or litigation?
- If arbitration, under what rules will the arbitration be based?

- Where does my claim or lawsuit need to be filed?

3.3 The Most Important "Rule"

Sometimes it's what you don't do that causes the greatest harm. That is the case when you fail to give proper notice when required by the contract. This is the one area where contractors typically get it wrong. But just what is this thing called "notice"? I like the following definition.

> **Notice: A communication seeking to make its recipient aware of a fact or thing, as required by law or contract.**
>
> *(Your Dictionary)*

Notice is a very specific type of communication with its own set of requirements that are usually spelled out in the contract. In order for a notice to be considered proper or valid, construction contracts typically define the following characteristics of a notice:

- Must be written
- Timing of delivery
- Form of delivery
- Person to be notified

In addition, you should be aware that while the main notice requirement of a contract may specify that notice of an event must be given in time to allow the general contractor (in the case of a contractor/subcontractor agreement) time to deliver his notice to the owner within 5 days of an event, there will probably be additional notice requirements throughout a contract for different circumstances affecting the work. The requirements for those other situations may not be the same as the general notice requirement. For instance, you may be required to give notice within 3 days of an event that would result in a delay. In another contract provision concerning changes, you might be required to submit notice of an increase in cost within 7 days from the time when a revision to the

39

contract documents is issued, or your right to receive extra compensation for the work is voided. In another clause, the contract may require you to respond within 48 hours to a non-conformance notice or you may be subject to back-charges from supplementation of your work by others. The point is, the notice requirement will probably vary throughout the contract, depending on the situation.

As you can see, the notice requirement is everywhere throughout the contract. That is why it is so easy to fail to give proper notice if you don't use the contract as a tool to manage your work. This also serves to emphasize the benefit of completing the Contract "Rules" Checklist which gives you a handy reference for all of these separate notice requirements in one list.

The existence of the notice requirement in your contracts is the main reason why you need to document events throughout the project – it is required by contract!

> *Providing timely notice reduces your risks and increases your chances of getting paid for all of your work.*

3.4 Why Don't You Give Notice?

The majority of contractors I have known don't like to give notice; they simply don't enjoy having to document their work. After all, construction should be about building things, not writing about them, right? Oh, if only it could be that simple.

Construction is full of risk. There are design risks, unforeseen event risks, risk of conflicts, and time delay risks to name just a few. And where those kinds of risks are present, over long duration, with commitments that are based on estimates, in a setting with many variables that are always changing, it is simply prudent to insist that events be documented in accordance with established rules so that risks can be identified and dealt with as much as possible.

So, why is it that contractors don't like to give notice or document their work? I think that the following reasons might be at the top of the list:

- Too busy running the job to write letters
- Low priority (don't see the urgency)
- Poor communication skills (not good with words)
- Don't know how
- Fear of the consequences

Let me expand on each one of these:

❖ Too busy running the job to write letters – I can relate to that. Managing construction can keep you extremely busy with all of the details that must be dealt with. However, I will show you in later chapters on writing that preparing effective communications is not complicated and does not have to be time consuming. Most people think of writing long letters and, as a result, they get bogged down in side issues, lose their focus, and adopt bad habits that make the job of communicating more difficult than it needs to be.

There may also be other reasons that you are busier than you should be due to deficiencies in managerial skills. Perhaps through the application of the PPRICK principles in this manual you may be able to correct some of those deficiencies.

❖ Low priority (don't see the urgency) – If this is your excuse, then it is due to your lack of understanding of the contract. Once you truly understand the specific obligations that the contract places on you (notice being one of them), you will see how the failure to document will directly result in greater risk of increased cost and time for your work. If you haven't been persuaded by now, as you proceed through the remainder of this manual you should see the connection between creating a good project record through proper documentation of the work and lower risk and increased profitability.

❖ <u>Poor communication skills (not good with words)</u> – I believe that this is probably more common in construction than in other types of work. This is especially true at the supervisory craft level (superintendents, general foremen, and foremen). Let's face it, we value the supervisory workers for their ability to get the job done, not for their writing skills. However, since they are at the front lines of the work, they can detect potential problems and see issues develop before anyone else does. This means that they are in a better position to create the required notice and to leave behind a more accurate record of the project.

The sections of this manual on effective writing (along with the examples provided throughout) will give anyone with poor communication skills the basic points they need to follow to produce quality correspondence with confidence.

❖ <u>Don't know how</u> – Many employees in construction today belong to a generation that has been raised in an environment where text messaging, and social media have been the main platforms for their communications. These employees are accustomed to writing (and thinking) in short blasts of text, often written in a short-hand abbreviated fashion that comes from the need to communicate quickly in those forums. As a result, their ability to communicate in complete and coherent sentences has suffered greatly through years of misuse. In a sad majority of the cases, they may never have acquired good writing skills at all. This is not totally their fault, as the educational system continues to place less emphasis on writing skills during their school years. They are partly a product of their times. I find that even college graduates are struggling when it comes to being able to write. If you think that I am exaggerating you should know that a national survey found that 23% of America is illiterate (as defined by demonstrating the basic skills that are acquired at the 4th grade level).[2]

Finally, another factor that influences one's ability to communicate coherently is being able to have continuity of thought. It seems that with all of the modern electronic communication devices at our disposal, our attention is interrupted more often and we are distracted much more frequently than ever before. This does not allow for the development of good communication skills. If you doubt what I am saying, try to have a meeting or conversation with someone today for 15 minutes and count the number of times that they check their messages or interrupt you to take incoming calls!

❖ Fear of the consequences – Most of the time when I ask contractors why they fail to document important issues the answer I am given fits into the "fear of the consequences" category. They usually say "it will make the customer angry", or "I don't want to start a paper war", or "I'm afraid I won't get my next progress payment", or even "I will be terminated if I do".

---

[2] Department of Education's National Adult Literacy Survey. The figures are for 2003, the latest year available for this survey. The survey tested three areas of literacy; prose, document, and quantitative.

If thoughts like these have crossed your mind, then you need to remind yourself of the following:

- Giving notice is <u>a requirement of the contract</u>.
- Failing to provide notice will probably shut the door to any potential recovery in the future for the extra cost or time due to changes or delays.
- Documenting issues that may extend your performance time is the best way to build the record that will help you defend against liquidated damages if the project is delayed.
- Failing to document will expose you to assessment of back-charges that you may not deserve.
- You can give notice of serious issues **_and_** at the same time be cooperative and helpful to your customer. I will show you how.
- Whether or not you document and give notice of issues, your customer will not let you off the hook if you fail to perform as required by the contract. <u>*You will receive notices from your customer regardless of whether you do or don't issue notices to them*</u>!

3.5 *Applying the "Rules"*

In order to be able to apply the rules in the contract to the management of the project, you must first be aware of the importance of knowing the contract and the fact that it contains the rules that are needed for project management.

Next, it is important to know where the specific rules are found in the contract for the particular situations that develop during the execution of the work. That was explained earlier in this chapter. The review of the contract to extract those specific rules should result in the completed Contract Rules Checklist which I introduced in section 3.1.

Application of the rules to project management should work like this:

1. Identify the circumstance, situation or issue that needs to be decided or acted upon,

2. Ask yourself, "what does the contract say (or require) in this situation?"

3. When you write about this issue, make sure to do so within the time required by the contract and explain how your actions or decisions comply with the requirements of the contract.

I will give you a more specific framework to use in determining when, what, and how to document in the coming chapters, but for now let's use the steps above to see how this works in a couple of common examples.

Example 3.5.1: Your General Superintendent notices at the beginning of the subcontractor meeting that neither the plumbing nor the mechanical subcontractors have their project representatives in attendance. Having reviewed the subcontracts, he knows that attendance at these meetings is mandatory. He makes sure that this deficiency is noted and recorded in the minutes of the meeting for distribution. Later, after the meeting, the General Superintendent takes a look at the Contract Rules Checklist and sees that there is also a $500 penalty that needs to be assessed against each of the subcontractors for failure to attend the meeting.

He writes a quick email to the project managers for the two companies and notifies them that their failure to attend this week's meeting has resulted in a $500 deduct change order to their subcontracts (citing the paragraph or clause from the subcontract). He also advises them that they need to be present at all future meetings, reminding them that failure to attend 3 meetings will be reason to demand their replacement (citing the specific article in the subcontract addressing that point).

He closes by stating that their absence at the subcontractor meeting makes it more difficult for the GC to manage the project and to coordinate the work of all subcontractors – thus, the reason for the mandatory attendance clause in the subcontract.

This communication did not take more than a few minutes and did not require a re-reading of the subcontracts, just a quick glance at the Rules Checklist that we discussed in section 3.1.

Example 3.5.2: You are the electrical subcontractor on a project. Your foreman is frustrated because heavy rain during the past few days caused by a tropical storm made it impossible for his crew to install the underground duct bank that is required before the foundations can be installed for the building. His work is now behind schedule and he is complaining to you (the project manager) about the fact that he will not be done on the required date. You realize that you have two options, you can take advantage of good weather days and work later on those days to catch up, or you can continue to work your current schedule and be late with the duct bank. You discuss this matter with the GC and he tells you that you should go on overtime to catch up now that there is good weather. He also tells you that you will get paid your extra cost for labor if you submit the bills to him with your next payment application.

You want to start the overtime work right away so you can make up for the delay, but you remember to ask yourself, "What does the contract say with respect to overtime work and weather delays?" You refer to your Contract Rules Checklist and quickly determine that weather delays must be noted in writing within 5 days and that your company will be paid for the extra cost of labor for overtime work (so long as it is not your fault) when you have been directed by the GC in writing to work overtime.

In order to save time, you prepare a notice to the GC citing the dates on which the rain affected your work and you explain the effect (how it washed out the trenches and caused your workers to re-work the duct banks). You include a couple of pictures, one of an open trench prior to the rains, and another of a trench that was washed out and had to be re-dug). In addition, you include copies of your daily field reports in which your foreman recorded the fact that the work was stopped by heavy rains on several days. You also provide the additional hourly costs for the overtime (in accordance with the contract clause that state how those costs are to be calculated for compensation). Finally, since you noticed that the overtime must be approved or directed by the GC, you provide a place in your letter for the GC's approval to comply with the contract. You hand deliver your letter to the GC.

Applying the rules from the contract begins in the field with supervisory personnel. Earlier I mentioned that your foremen and superintendents are the ones at the front lines of the action. Sometimes, due to the short time frame provided by the notice requirement of the contract, it's those employees that must be sensitive to the need to document the work in order for you to be able comply on time. For this reason, it is very important to educate all project supervisors on the contract requirements (the rules). They should understand what conditions or situations to look for, what needs to be documented, when to document, how to document, and why it is important.

Many companies provide training for their managerial staff, but often stop at the project management level. They fail to see the importance of having superintendents and foremen that are knowledgeable of key contract requirements for administration of the work. They believe that the field supervisors' work only requires them to know the technical aspects of the contract. That approach fails to take advantage of some of the most valuable resources at your disposal and can lead to many situations where you end up compromising your ability to reduce risk and maximize profit.

The typical project manager for a general contractor spends the majority of the time in the office, buried deep in administration; planning, coordinating, reporting, deciding issues, and dealing with subcontractor, vendor, and customer interactions. The time available for field observation or inspection of the work can be quite short, which is one of the reasons that various field superintendents are employed for key aspects of the work. It follows therefore, that these field superintendents will be intimately more aware of the details and will see situations develop before the project manager can take notice.

In the case of a subcontractor, that advantage is even more pronounced. Unless the size of the project is significant, the subcontractor's project manager may not be on the jobsite other than for the required weekly meeting or for larger problems that must be observed first hand. That being the case, it is the general foreman or foremen on the jobsite that will have the day-to-day knowledge of issues and developments which could impact the bottom line.

Even on jobs that warrant an on-site superintendent, the role of that individual is usually focused on labor productivity and not on the management of contract risks. With this kind of arrangement, it is therefore very easy to miss the window of time that is required for proper notice of key events that will affect profitability on the job.

On the larger projects that justify a project manager in the field, I have often seen where the management effectiveness of that individual is diluted by many factors such as: having management responsibility over more than one job, lack of support staff, and over-burdening the manager with home office administrative tasks or estimating other work that detracts from the management of the project.

How can your field supervision assist in applying the contract rules to manage the project better? To start with, they should be sensitive to spot any development or condition that could:

- Enlarge the scope of the work
- Increase the cost of the work
- Extend the time of performance

Below are some examples that would fall into these categories:

1. Spot field conditions that are different than what the Contract Documents represented.
2. Look for changes in design (scope) when drawing revisions, supplemental instructions, field sketches, bulletins, memoranda, clarifications, responses to RFI's, or directives are issued.
3. Be aware of the schedule and track the work to the schedule, especially those activities that precede your work and note when any of them are delayed which could delay the start of your work activities.

4. Be aware of the start date of your work activities and note any delays in receiving requested information (RFI responses), shop drawing approvals, Change Orders, and other direction necessary for the start of your activities.

5. Be aware of weather delays and record them.

6. Note any condition or situation that develops which interferes with your ability to perform your work (incomplete or improper work by other subcontractors, lack of access, inadequate vertical transportation, debris, crowded working conditions, multiple trades working out of sequence, or inspection issues).

7. Note any condition or situation that requires a re-sequencing of your work.

8. Request written confirmation (in accordance with the contract) of all verbal instructions or directives that involve additional work or changes to the work in the Contract Documents.

Having identified those situations or events, some or all of the following action should then be taken by the field staff:

a) Create a field memo to document differing field conditions (citing specifics, including photos when appropriate).

b) Compare any new document received with Contract Documents and create an internal memo to document changes for the project manager.

c) Create an internal memo to document any delay or potential delay to work activities to alert the project manager.

d) Create a field memo to document interference with the ability to perform the work (citing specifics, including photos when appropriate).

e) Insert comments in Daily Field Report.

f) Report all conditions noted at the subcontractor meetings.

Once the field staff has identified the problem and created a record of it, then it's up to the project manager to follow-through with additional action as warranted. For example, it may be more appropriate for a notice of delay to originate with the project manager as opposed to the field superintendent or area foreman (it may also be required by contract). Many companies believe in keeping the field employees out of the way of documenting issues that could create animosity or lead to contract disputes. However, there is nothing wrong with including a memo from the superintendent or several Daily Reports that cite the problems in the project manager's notification of a delay.

The key to avoiding animosity is to keep the correspondence focused on the facts as they affect performance, and not make the issue personal, keeping the tone of all communication professional. I will have more to say about this in the chapters on effective communications (chapters 8 and 9).

If your project management practice has been one that relied on verbal communications and persuasion, resorting to documentation only when all other means failed, you may find it awkward when you try doing it at first. However, like anything worth doing, once you develop the habit of following the contract "rules" you will start to see the benefits. As with any habit, after a while, documenting issues will become second nature to you.

I can't begin to count the number of times that I have shown contractors how they could have avoided or lessened the severity of their problems if they had only communicated the issues in writing *while they occurred during the job*, rather than wait for them to escalate into full blown crises to begin to document their side of the issues. The result is always worse when there was a failure to document the work.

What is amazing to me is that although contractors may see the error of their ways with hindsight, few will correct their mistakes on the next project. I know I'm repeating myself, but it bears restating that **_what is common sense is not common practice!_**

3.6 *Make Others Follow the Rules*

How many times have you started performing extra work on the promise of a change only to find that getting that change in writing took longer and was more difficult than you expected? And be honest, don't you find it harder to receive the fair price for a change once you have done the majority of the work? Do you ever wonder why it seems that you can't get many of your changes approved until the end of most projects?

What takes place in these situations is that you lose pricing leverage when you have performed the work and then try to negotiate after the fact. All contracts I have seen contain a clause that requires all changes to the contract to be performed after written approval. In nearly all cases there is also the requirement to have a price and time for the change established at the time of approval. In cases where a price or time cannot be agreed upon prior to the approval of the changed work, then at least a mechanism is in place to arrive at an agreed upon value of the work by using a formula for cost and markup that is specified in the contract.

However, on nearly all projects it seems like there is a concerted effort to violate this rule of the contract, whether for reason of "expediency", or because we have established "good will", it matters not. There is simply no reason for you to fall for this loosening of the rules of the contract when it comes to changes in the work. At least not for the minimum requirement that a written document should be issued to authorize the change with the understanding that it will cost more money and time (if that is the case) and to require a minimum time period to have those variables agreed upon.

To work on changes without approval is a violation of one of the basic rules of the contract. If the proposed change is not approved, you will have to uninstall the work (at your cost) in order to conform to the Contract Documents that are approved for construction. If you are ever asked to work on changes without a written approval you can be sure that there is either no firm decision yet on the part of the owner to approve the change, or there is another motivation which is probably not in your best interest. Don't do it! Simply refer to the rules in the contract and insist that the other side follow the rules. In fact, when you think about this situation, it doesn't make any sense!

Ask yourself, since the other side probably wrote or chose the language in the contract, why would they want to break their own rules?

As for the approval on the amount and additional time for the changed work, that is a different story, as there could be many legitimate reasons for lack of agreement. Even so, there should be no reason to delay agreement on those factors any longer than necessary. Certainly, once the extra work has commenced in earnest, there should be a mechanism in place to compensate you for the cost of that work. If you will read the section of your contracts pertaining to extra work you will find that most of them contain a provision for compensation in the event there is no agreement on cost (typically a "forced work" or "directive" option).

Change Orders are an area where contractors are most often abused, especially at the subcontractor level. Think about the benefit to the owner or the party with the obligation to finance the work. The longer they can delay the approval of the change, while the changed work is progressing, the less the amount of financing that will be needed, and the lower the financing costs. In fact, the additional work done under changes that are not yet approved will be performed at the expense of the subcontractors and contractor that have performed the work without pay. I believe therein lies the reason for the majority of extra work disputes on many jobs which are not given the attention they deserve until after the projects are completed.

I mentioned above that you must get your changes approved in writing before you start the work. There are steps that you can take to maximize your chances of reaching agreement on the changed work and to get paid during their performance. In order to be successful in this area, sometimes you may need to be more persistent or assertive than you might have been in the past. Here is my advice:

1. Price the extra work fairly and accurately: To begin with, you should try your best to make sure that your request for cost and time for the proposed change is complete, accurate and priced in accordance with your contract. Also, you should price the work fairly, that is, if a credit needs to be given for portions of work deleted, give it. I have seen many cases where contractors grossly inflate the costs in their change order requests and are later shocked or insulted when the request is rejected. You need to eliminate any reason for the reviewer to reject it or delay its approval based on something that is obviously incorrect or not in accordance with the contract. Those kind of thoughtless mistakes will only delay review and approval of your change request.

2. Include all necessary justification for the change: Many of the change order requests that I have seen fall short in this category. They often lack a simple explanation of how or why the extra cost arises. Sometimes it can be as easy as including marked up drawings identifying the changes. Other times a step by step narrative may be required with pictures of the field conditions. The point is that you should provide as much evidence as possible to the other side that will allow them to agree with your point of view for the justification of the added cost (and time). In addition to being the reasonable thing to do, it is usually explicitly required in the contract.

3. Provide an expiration date for the pricing of your proposal: You should include a date through which your proposal is valid. This date should also allow a reasonable time for someone to review your proposal.

4. Don't start any of the work without written authorization: There are no exceptions to this! Remember, it is required by contract.

5. Follow up your request: You will need to send frequent inquiries on the status of your change order request. These should be in writing. Your first inquiry should be a few days before the expiration date you gave on your proposal. That inquiry should state that if you don't receive approval in time you will be re-visiting the proposal to see if the prices are still valid and you will re-submit in the event there are any changes (this also applies to field conditions that may have changed).

6. If you received a notice to proceed but the amount of the change, or additional time is still pending, you need to be even more diligent in your follow-up. You should consider communicating that you will allow the other side a reasonable period of time to review your offer, after which you request a face-to-face meeting to negotiate the change.

7. If after your efforts to request a meeting or if your meeting reaches no resolution of the change, then you need to invoke the dispute resolution clause of the contract and submit your demand in a claim for the amount (and time) that you had requested for the change. Your claim should clearly state that you will follow the procedure in your contract for resolution of the dispute by whatever means the contract calls for (arbitration or litigation). Though this may seem like you are jumping the gun, you are not!

> *Your contract has a dispute resolution mechanism for a reason – to resolve disputes.*

Your contract does not say that you must wait until you complete your change order work (without payment) and then try to resolve the dispute after the job is complete, does it? You need to use the rules of the contract to get matters resolved during construction, while you need the cash flow that compensates for the added cost of the change. Many times I have noted that the mere mention of the desire to invoke the dispute resolution clause results in a more serious meeting to resolve pending change order disputes.

I must emphasize that I would not hesitate at all in taking this last step if the extra work in question was being performed under protest (i.e. if there was a construction directive or forced work order issued that does not acknowledge extra compensation or time for the work).

I hope you can see from the preceding example how the rules in the contract can be used to have others follow the rules as well (to your benefit). It's important for you to keep in mind that while you may need to be more assertive with your demands to address legitimate extra work requests, you need to do so in a manner that is professional and not combative. There is a world of difference between being persistently direct and badgering or antagonizing in your approach. I will go into more detail on this topic when I give you specific advice for writing in chapters 7 and 8.

Remember, the Rules Can be Used Both Ways!

Early in my career, I was involved in a hospital renovation project with a large national general contractor. During the first part of the job, my company was receiving letters every day. Most of the letters were about trivial items, demanding we take care of them right away. It appeared that the GC was building a paper trail in order to back-charge us at the end of the job.

While in the GC's trailer one day, I noticed they had several notebooks of company procedures that dealt with each item of work and each article of their contract. Out of curiosity, I asked if I could look through their manuals, and it was there that the light clicked on for me!

From that point on I began to look at my contract in a different way; I started looking for all clauses or conditions for which the GC had a responsibility to me! I made sure to address any legitimate issue he had pointed out, but I started to write to the GC about those problems we were encountering where they had failed in their responsibility to our company. After a few of these letters, I was called to a special meeting by the project manager. It was obvious my letters had made an impact.

The GC agreed to stop writing about trivial issues and our relationship improved.

CHAPTER FOUR

Perform

$\underline{P}$ PRICK

4.1 There is no Substitute for Performance

The first step in guaranteeing success in any endeavor is to perform. The construction field is no different. Your contracts demand a certain level of performance. If you are not good at what you do, you will not reap the rewards of your efforts, no matter how hard you try. The losses on your jobs will drive you out of business, if your poor reputation doesn't do that first.

I define optimum performance in construction as follows:

> **Build your contract scope,**
> **at the lowest cost,**
> **within the allowed contract time.**

I think you would agree with me that a project manager who adopts this definition of performance in his job should have a high degree of success. That would be the kind of project manager everyone would want to hire for their construction business.

Once you understand and accept this definition, then it becomes easy to see how anything that affects the scope of work (whether enlarging, modifying, interfering with, or accelerating it) could present a problem. Likewise, any condition that increases the cost of the work should be considered a problem. Finally, anything that threatens to extend the time for completing the work should be viewed the same way.

If you apply this framework to project documentation, then it facilitates the identification of those events and situations that should be recorded during construction. You can also see that by adopting this way of thinking for project management, the motivation and justification is there to document anything that gets in the way of optimum performance. It stands to reason then, that the main focus of your communication in construction should be on performance.

4.2 *Don't Cause Self-Inflicted Damage*

In the prior section I defined optimum performance and a way of thinking that should guide a project manager in that direction. Now, I need to spend some time describing the consequences of performance failures. Whether or not we are able to achieve optimum performance, it is essential that you meet the required minimum performance standards of the contract. Failure to do so will invite problems and increase risk at your expense; what I call self-inflicted damage. Performance failure or non-performance should be avoided at all cost.

In the last chapter I talked about how to find and apply the rules from the contract to document the issues that affect your work (increasing your scope, cost and time). I also mentioned that the contract rules work both ways. When you fail to perform, you will be on the receiving end of notices for your non-performance or defective work. You should also be aware that the typical contract contains rules that dictate the requirements for your response to those notices as well.

Many times contractors ignore or place a low priority on these types of notices from their customer and, as a result, they get burned a short while later. The damage many times comes by surprise with the appearance of another contractor to supplement your work, or by a notice of non-performance to your bonding company, or even with receipt of a notice of termination. This can happen very quickly in accordance with the timing determined by those nasty "rules" in your contract that you may not have read.

Being on the receiving end of these kinds of notices greatly increases your risks on the project, placing your company on the path to higher costs and lower profits (or losses). If you receive this type of notice you must be very careful, as this can be a very slippery slope.

We know there is a natural tendency for people to look for someone to blame whenever things are not going well. If your company has been a habitual non-performer on a project, it can become the scapegoat for problems, making it easy for others to use it as the source of their problems. Remember, companies take action based in part on the opinions and judgments of individuals who are subject to biases based on perceptions that may not be fair or accurate. I am sure you are familiar with this "piling on" effect from other experiences in your life.

Those notices of non-performance become part of the project record which can color one's impression on other issues that may be unrelated. For example, it can be more difficult to obtain a reduction of your retainage on a project when your company was cited for a shortcoming in performance during an earlier period. You will probably experience a worse cash flow on the project than if you were not cited for performance deficiencies. Even getting approval for your proposed amount of extra cost for changes may prove to be more challenging if you have a prior record of non-performance.

There are many ways you start to lose your leverage on a project when you have demonstrated a record of poor performance. In cases where your deficiency occurs on a critical part of the project, or in the case of continued deficiencies, you will become the cause of delays to the project schedule and will find yourself defending costly liquidated damages at the end of the job.

It also stands to reason that an owner or general contractor would try to allocate more costs and back charges to your company at the completion of the project if it had been guilty of performance deficiencies throughout the job.

You may be thinking that meeting the performance standards in the contract is perfectly logical advice, and something that should not even need to be mentioned. That is great if your company is one that takes the time to read the contract, understand the requirements and works to stay out of trouble always. However, I have seen many contractors who don't take the requirements seriously, who think they can get by doing less, whose objective at times is to cut corners on performance to save cost. If that weren't bad enough, when they get caught and the notice is received, they are in disbelief or begin to argue their actions, all the while wasting valuable time that could be used to correct their work or cure the violation. That type of response is counter-productive and only worsens their position. By their conduct, these contractors appear to be good at causing self-inflicted damage.

When your company performs on a project, you are reducing the risk over time that any of the punitive clauses in the contract are exercised against you. It's as if you are able to neutralize those clauses to eliminate the liability that existed when you signed the contract. You take off the table any self-inflicted damage that you may create on your own. If your performance is good, all you need to worry about are the actions of others and how they might affect your work. To use a football analogy, even though your offense can score lots of points, if you want to be assured of victory, you need to have a good defense (avoiding turnovers will help too).

Good performance is absolutely essential in construction because if you don't perform, those performance failures will diminish your leverage and restrict your chances of recovering any legitimate claims your company may have.

4.3 Don't Try to Fake Performance

> *"Oh what a tangled web we weave,*
> *when first we practice to deceive."*
> *(Sir Walter Scott)*

We have all exaggerated, stretched the truth a bit, told a white lie at times, and given excuses that were not valid. These may all be normal inclinations for our initial response whenever we find ourselves in situations where we have failed or fell short of expectations. However, there can be danger in this behavior when it is applied to construction documentation.

Say you receive a notice telling you that your performance on a specific activity or area of a project is not keeping up with the plan and you are also requested to respond in writing with a performance commitment or a target manpower level. You should keep in mind that your actual performance will be measured and judged against your written commitment or target. That is not the time for wishful thinking or promises based on ideal conditions. Doing that will only set yourself up for a second notice, and more severe scrutiny (and consequences), since you will be bound to fall short of the expectations once again. However, this time the failure will be in comparison with your own (unrealistic) stated commitments.

The same holds true for stretching the truth or giving excuses meant to redirect the blame. You are bound to be caught. Your story or excuse most likely won't stand up to the facts in the light of day. I find it very predictable whenever I hear contractors tell me that they were only "trying to buy time" with this story or that excuse. The reality is that the stories you tell will turn out to be without merit <u>and</u> you will have to bite the bullet and take the corrective steps that are necessary to get out of the trouble you are in regardless of your efforts to buy time. So I ask, why not pay the price early in the process, when it is bound to be less expensive, before you are branded as a non-performer <u>and</u> a <u>liar</u>? Sounds like common sense, right? Woops, there we go again. I think we're on to something.

The bottom line in all this: there is no substitute for performance, so don't try to fake it.

4.4 *It's Always Cheaper to Do it Right the First Time*

It's normal for contractors to try to find ways to cut costs, however, sometimes when these efforts become aggressive, there is a tendency to compromise on performance criteria with the end result being less than what is expected and required by contract. This is why I emphasize performance as a key principle in the "PPRICK" philosophy. A good project manager knows that cutting corners on performance in the desire to increase profit can result in costly corrective measures or re-work as a result of failing to meet the standards in the contract. In addition to the increased cost to correct or replace the work, there are the added costs of labor disruption and possible delays to other work that must be considered.

If you make it a practice to understand your contract requirements and to perform to the level that is necessary to meet (or exceed) them, you should not have to worry about having your work rejected or about having to go back to make corrections or re-install work that was already completed. Make this a part of your company philosophy, remind your employees often and make them accountable for failures when they occur. Performance failures are costly, time consuming, and can lead to larger problems, including the loss of reputation.

CHAPTER FIVE

Be Proactive

P**P**RICK

What does it mean to be **proactive**? It may be useful to take a look at some definitions:

> *Tending to initiate change rather than reacting to events.*
> *(World English Dictionary)*
>
> *Assuming an active, rather than passive, role in doing, accomplishing, etc.; taking the initiative.*
> *(Webster's New World Dictionary)*

An experienced project manager will have accumulated a history of many different situations from prior projects. He should be able to recognize when a series of events starts to resemble a prior situation and draw from his mental inventory of the prior actions taken and the results from those experiences, to apply to the current problem he faces. By doing this, he can utilize his prior experience to anticipate future situations that may arrive and adjust his plans accordingly.

5.1 Adopt a Forward-Looking Attitude

To be a proactive manager you must be able to look into the future, anticipate events, and plan for your desired result, as you take care of your current work. You need to prepare every aspect of your work before it is time to perform. You must plan your resources: materials, labor and equipment well before they are needed. Finally, utilizing your experience, you should anticipate potential problems and their solution when you make your plans.

If you are involved in the business of managing construction and find that you are constantly reacting to yesterday's events, unable to look beyond tomorrow, you need to change your ways. You need to begin by adopting a different way of thinking.

> *When you don't have a plan for where you want to go, you will end up nowhere, or worse, wherever others decide to take you.*

While it is true that project management often deals with the management of unexpected events, the best managers seem to experience less of them than others. That is not by coincidence. A proactive manager develops the habit of planning every aspect of the work ahead of time. Then, the manager makes sure that the plan is executed to achieve the intended results. Nothing is left to chance.

In addition to making detailed plans for his company's work, a proactive manager is also minimizing risk through careful observation and anticipation of problems that can derail his plans. He gives others the benefit of time to correct the problems through early documenting of potential issues before they have a significant effect on his work. This can reduce the number of issues that will have impact, thereby reducing the risk posed by those issues.

There will be times of course, when despite being proactive in documenting the potential problem, there may be no improvement in the condition and the issue ends up affecting the work. The advantage to having documented the potential problem is that you will have left a record which will help to keep you from being blamed (without justification) for the problem at a later date.

When you plan ahead, both for the anticipated and the unexpected, you are less likely to be surprised or caught off guard when the unexpected arrives. You will have a reasoned response plan, rather than a knee jerk reaction that you may later regret. This is one of the reasons why it is prudent to have a plan "B" (or contingency plan) for critical points of the work on a project.

By taking the time to prepare as I have described, you will be able to navigate quickly through the problems with less undesirable impacts.

5.2 *Identify What is Important and Set Priorities*

Let's take a look at some practical steps you can take to enhance your preparation when planning the work. When it comes to being proactive in managing a project, the schedule should be your main tool.

- Your primary focus should be on the critical path – your plans should take into considerations the submittals, material procurement, manpower, tools and equipment necessary to support the work activities that lie on the critical path.

- Pay special attention to details and events that could have a large impact on the cost and time of performance of the activities on the critical path.

- Your daily, weekly, and longer range plans should all focus on ensuring that your activities that run through the critical path are able to be executed without a hitch when the time comes to perform.

- Set up reminders, work outlines, check lists, and other progress steps to review with subordinates. Don't take any of your plans for granted, make sure to follow-through periodically to confirm that you are getting the outcomes you desire.

Next, you should identify the work of others that precedes your key (critical path) activities and set up a procedure to monitor the progress of that work.

- This could be as simple a system as taking a project schedule and hi-lighting the precedent activities, then periodically noting the progress of those activities on that schedule.

- Whenever the pace of a precedent work activity appears to be threatening the start of your work, you need to send documentation to your customer to forewarn of the potential delay to your work. Think of this as an early warning system. It should be done in a constructive manner to assist others in managing the overall project.

- As part of your documentation, sometimes it is important to include photographs of a condition in order to record it accurately and to be able to demonstrate to others the conflict or problem that exists.

- Proactive management also requires active participation in all weekly job meetings. It is important to make sure that others are alerted to potential problems you see and to insist that some corrective action be taken while there is still time. When the minutes of the meetings are issued, you need to make sure that they accurately state what took place during the meeting, issuing corrections for items that were misstated or omitted from the minutes. Remember, what is not recorded may be regarded as not having existed or forgotten, when looking back at the end of the job.

Prioritize your work and resources on a daily and weekly basis to achieve critical milestones.

- Project management should not be a haphazard enterprise. You should have a clear plan of work and a breakdown of tasks for accomplishing it. The best project managers are masters of their time. Having your priorities organized and clearly stated in your plan will help you to be efficient in the use of your time.

- There are many inexpensive tools available to make the work of planning, prioritizing, and task management easier. A proactive manager will take advantage of these tools to simplify his work. This is an area where technological tools (e.g. task management and scheduling software for smart phones and tablets) are of great benefit, especially when they share a common platform that allows for updating from any one source.

As I said earlier there may be times when even with the best planning and task management efforts, it is not possible to avoid the problems that impact your work. Being proactive also means knowing when to ask for help. Some of these situations may overwhelm your ability and stretch your management capacity. It is imperative that you request additional support or resources in those cases when you see the situation worsening, in order to avoid having it become critical and producing negative effects on the work or the schedule.

5.3 *Take the Initiative – Proactive Documentation*

When you adopt the proactive attitude to project management, you don't wait for things to happen, you make them happen. You don't hope that circumstances will change or improve; you take action to create the change or improvement you desire.

Taking the initiative on key issues can make the difference between having your input considered in the resolution of a problem, and having to accept a solution that others proposed without your consideration, one that may actually put you at a disadvantage.

When you take the initiative to offer a solution to a problem, you demonstrate that you are a team player and build up good will with your customer. Many times by offering the solution, you are able to save others valuable time and precious resources. By doing so, you may also be able to advance a solution that fits your needs better than others.

Whenever you document conditions proactively, you are calling the attention of others to potential problems. While this may "ruffle the feathers" of some (namely, those who are the cause of the potential problem), it should be welcomed by other project participants, since it will give them the added benefit of more time to circumvent the problem. When done in a cooperative manner, proactive documentation can be a win-win strategy. You end up creating a record which will demonstrate later how a problem came about, and others will receive an early warning that could help them avoid a crisis. You should think of proactive documentation as a method of helping others on the project so they can help you achieve your goals.

5.4 Documenting From the Front Lines:
The Daily Report

Perhaps the place where contractors miss their best opportunity to be proactive in their documentation is in their Daily Reports. This document, usually required by contract, is the only daily document your company prepares for its projects. The Daily Report is typically completed by your field superintendent or general foreman at the jobsite. These are your representatives that are at the front lines of the work, closest to the action.

Most contractors don't pay attention to what their field employees enter in their Daily Reports. As a result, the information recorded in these reports is sporadic, inconsistent, lacking in detail, and often meaningless or irrelevant. In many companies the attitude towards the Daily Report is one of indifference. They consider the document a nuisance, paperwork that must be filled out and turned in; a waste of valuable time for their field supervisors.

Whenever I come across those situations I think of the opportunities that were missed and of the additional burdens that have been created as a result! Your see, as the only daily document, prepared closest to events by people in the know, the Daily Report is the best source for collecting accurate data for later use in preparing a detailed history of your work on the project. When you think of the entire collection of all the records that are generated during the course of a project, the Daily Reports are the backbone; the roadmap that will tell the history to guide you through the events from start to finish.

Daily Reports can serve a variety of purposes for you during construction. In addition to meeting the requirements of the contract, they can benefit you as follows:

- Document the weather conditions at the project site
- Create a detailed record of your company's work on the project

- Provide you an early warning of potential delays to your work
- Serve to document problems or conflicts which can affect your plan
- Provide you an early record of changes that may be necessary
- Record impacts to your labor productivity
- Substantiate time and material work on extras

While your Daily Report may not satisfy the notice requirement of your contract, it can serve as support and assist you in preparing your notice correspondence. It is important that all Daily Reports are forwarded to your company's office for safekeeping and for review by a manger responsible for the project so appropriate, timely action can be taken as required by the contract.

Daily Reports can also serve a dual purpose when they contain the data that is needed for payroll. They can also be configured to provide detailed activity information that matches the schedule so that there is no question what work was being performed on any given day by each employee. These types of reports are more appropriate for larger projects, where employees are more likely to be assigned to tasks for longer periods of time as opposed to smaller jobs where they may be bouncing between several tasks on a given day.

I have found that when Requests for Change Orders are supported by Daily Reports that cite the conditions that changed (or the conflicts that were encountered), the response is more favorable due to the credibility that is afforded to these contemporaneous documents.

Having spent countless hours poring through documents on many projects after completion, in order to prepare an accurate record of events that will reveal the cause and effect that form the basis of most claims, I can tell you that my effort is facilitated when I find consistent Daily Reports that were prepared with the required detail. When there are good Daily Reports, supplemented with occasional photos of the work and periodic documentation of issues, my task is simplified greatly. More importantly, the outcome is always superior.

Finally, I have seen the great weight that is placed on the Daily Reports by judges and arbitrators, especially when the author of the report is able to testify about the facts that were recorded in them. If you ever have to rely on any document for proof of facts, the Daily Report is the one that you should have to include the facts.

CHAPTER SIX

Be Responsive

P P **R** I C K

6.1 Why You Need to Respond

There are many different types of notices that you may receive during the course of your involvement on a construction project. Some of the more common types of notices you might receive requiring a response are:

- insufficient manpower,
- defective work,
- delay,
- re-sequencing,
- fragmented work,
- revised schedule,
- force work directive,
- stop work

All of these notices have one thing in common, they may affect your scope, cost or time. Your failure to respond to them may result in unintended consequences like:

- losing certain rights provided to you in the contract
- losing options that you would otherwise have for response
- setting yourself up for a worse problem
- allowing others to create a one-sided record of your performance
- losing control over part or all of the work

6.2 *Overcome Procrastination*

It makes sense to take care of your own problems early, whenever they are brought to your attention, before they turn into expensive liabilities. In chapter 3 the reasons why you don't document were discussed. In a similar manner, I will go through the reasons why you procrastinate in responding to notices and attempt to show you how to overcome this problem.

I suppose that if I asked enough of you the reason why you procrastinate, I would get a list of responses like this:

- I don't take notices seriously, the problem will go away on its own
- I don't see the importance to respond
- I might make the situation worse if I respond
- I don't know how to respond

Let me address these objections and point out the flaws in each one so that you will be able to respond in the future.

- <u>I don't take notices seriously, the problem will go away on its own</u>: First of all, the fact that you received a written notice of a problem is an indication that it should be taken seriously. Remember, the party that sent you the notice has more productive things to do than to write notices to you. If you happen to subscribe to this approach it is because you don't understand that a notice is the required first step (on the part of the person issuing it) before action can be taken against you. In my years of experience covering a multitude of projects and issues, I don't remember any problem that went away on its own after a notice was issued. Believe me, by waiting to respond you will only make matters worse for yourself.

- <u>I don't see the importance to respond</u>: If you are thinking along these lines it is most likely due to your lack of knowledge of the contract. A review of the contract provision related to the notice should provide you with the motivation to respond quickly!

- <u>I might make the situation worse if I respond</u>: This line of thinking is due to the general fear you may have of documenting issues. You believe that once you start to write about a problem it will escalate the issue and cause more problems for you on the project. At the root of your fear is usually the fact that you don't know what's in your contract. If you did, you would realize that you need to respond to notices for many reasons, depending on the situation. A response may be required by the contract to AVOID making the problem worse! In many cases a response is needed in order to set the record straight, when the other party is incorrect in its statements or position. In all cases, knowledge of the contract will eliminate this fear.

  Another reason you may have this fear is that when you write about a problem, especially in defending your position, you usually do so in a confrontational manner. You write angry letters, using personal attacks and fail to address the facts. This approach will certainly escalate the issues and can only make matters worse with the other side, since it advances positions at the expense of constructive solutions. If you've had a tendency of taking this kind of approach in the past, perhaps it would help if you were to cool down before composing your thoughts for a response. Chapters 7 and 8 will also provide you with suggested steps to follow and pitfalls to avoid in preparing your communication.

- <u>I don't know how to respond</u>: If this is your situation, then the solution is two-fold. First you need to review and understand your contract to see how the notice you received must be dealt with. The second part of the solution is to learn how to document in a manner that deals with the facts of the issue and shows how you are moving to resolve it. Chapters 8 & 9 address this in greater detail with examples.

The good news for all of the objections above is that the answer lies with either education (knowledge of the contract) or getting help (by acquiring the skills or by enlisting others) if you don't feel capable of responding on your own.

6.3 *Set the Record Straight*

Building a construction project is very detailed work. It often takes the efforts of dozens of companies, thousands of employees, tens of thousands of different materials, coming together to complete thousands of activities over a period of months or years in order to achieve the end product. This is an industry in which every activity no matter how small is recorded in order to keep track of the progress, to make appropriate payments, to forecast and plan for the work and to apportion damages when things go wrong (which they often do).

If you understand this, you will take the project record seriously. For all of these reasons, the information that makes it into the record should be accurate. Unfortunately, often it is not. Human nature tends to distort, enlarge and suppress information at times for selfish reasons or simply due to bias. We are all judged by our actions and our reputations. If the record of your actions while you are building the project does not reflect reality, that can have damaging consequences. Think of what could be at stake:

- Payment for your work
- Release of retainage
- Approval and payment for extra work
- Approval of contract time extension
- Termination of your contract
- Damages for delay
- Liquidated damages

To ignore the accuracy of your performance record could be damaging to your bottom line. Here are some practical steps you can take to ensure that the record is accurate:

1. Always make the effort to correct in writing any inaccurate statements about your work or your performance that is written by others. The minutes of meetings are typical documents that may need to be corrected from time to time. It is simply not enough to voice your objection with the record during the project meeting. You must follow-up by reviewing the minutes to ensure that your correction of

the record was recorded properly in the minutes. I always made the point of sending a short memo to confirm my objection with any inaccurate record or omission that I saw in the minutes after attending the jobsite meeting.

2. Respond to inaccurate or baseless charges or statements about your company. Do not let improper accusations go unanswered. When responding, do not get personal or resort to emotional arguments, simply correct the statement with the facts as you understand them, and if the incorrect accusation was serious, ask for a retraction. You may not get an acknowledgement, apology, or retraction from the other side, but at least the record will not be silent which could later be interpreted by others that the accusation may have been true.

3. Many times contractors issue notices about deficiencies in the work of a trade which may not be deficiencies at all, but instead are due to conditions that develop as a result of other factors that end up appearing to be a shortage of manpower or a delay in performance. A common example of this is when a project has experienced a structural delay in an area and then the decision is made to accelerate the framing work. Suddenly (yes, it could happen overnight) the wall framing is complete in that area of the project and a notice is received by the MEP trades that they are behind schedule and they must accelerate their performance to "catch up" with the wall rough-ins. Even if this situation does not pose a manpower problem for the MEP trades affected, the characterization of the notice is incorrect, since the need to accelerate is not due to any deficiency on the part of the MEP trades. The record should be corrected to state the true reason for the need to accelerate the MEP work; the fact that the structural delay had caused the successor work activities to fall behind schedule. As you can see, it is easy to twist the facts when making up the project record to suit a specific party. You should take the time to read all correspondence and meeting minutes carefully to make sure that they reflect the facts and not someone's agenda at your expense.

CHAPTER SEVEN

Write to Inform

P P R I C K

To be able to work in the construction industry you should be prepared to immerse yourself in tremendous amounts of detail. The management of issues and circumstances that arise are dependent on and involve many facts. Most of the writing that is necessary in construction serves one or more of the following purposes:

1. To inform others of problem situations – conveying facts, describing problems, options, cost, etc. in order to facilitate solutions that allow the project to continue in the direction and at the pace that was planned.

2. To record progress.

3. To create an accurate record of the facts and events that can be woven together to produce a reliable history of the project.

7.1 Focus on Performance When Writing About Problems

When preparing to write about an issue or a problem, ask yourself the following questions:

> ➢ **What** is the **issue** or problem?

> ➢ **Why (or how)** does that **impact** the **scope** and/or **time** to perform?

Think of this as the "what" and "why" of your message.

Let me give some examples of how this works for various issues from the different perspectives of a general contractor and subcontractor (based on different facts of course).

1. **Issue: Delay to a critical activity**

If you are a general contractor, you may need to point out how the lack of progress being made by the electrical contractor on the installation of the main distribution system of the project *[the issue or problem]* is affecting the rest of the work activities that depend on that work, specifically the energizing of power for testing the mechanical equipment in the buildings. In addition, you would explain that this work is on the critical path and that any delays to the project schedule (if not recovered) will result in liquidated damages to be assessed from the electrical contractor *[the impact]*.

If you are the electrical subcontractor, you may need to write about how interference or restricted access to your work *[the issue or problem]* is affecting and delaying the installation of the main distribution system of the project. In addition, you would explain that since this problem is not your fault, any acceleration or additional costs that are incurred from the need to accelerate will be requested as an extra to your contract *[the impact]*.

2. **Issue: Damage to installed work**

If you are a general contractor, you may need to notify the painting subcontractor that there is damage to completed walls that need to be repaired throughout areas of the project *[the issue or problem]*. Your notice should be accompanied by properly taken photographs that will clearly show the damage in question. You will want to note that the damage, if left unrepaired will delay the punch list in those areas, so another painter will be brought to the job to do the work if it is not started within 48 hours *[the impact]*.

If you are a painting subcontractor, you may need to state that the damage to the completed walls was done by other trades as a result of finished painting ordered to be performed out of sequence, before the other trades were complete in those areas *[the issue or problem]*. Since the problem is not your fault, you will require additional compensation for going back to repaint the areas that were damaged *[the impact]*.

3. Issue: Rejection of work installed

If you are a general contractor, you may need to notify the tile subcontractor that the work in the bathrooms was rejected by the architect since it does not comply with the standards set forth in the specifications *[the issue or problem]*. Your notice should include the requirement that the correction of the defective work must commence within 48 hours or the subcontractor will be in default in accordance with the subcontract *[the impact]*.

If you are the tile subcontractor, you will need to inform the general contractor that the drywall work in the bathrooms is not in accordance with the specifications *[the issue or problem]*, and that if you proceed to install your tile as requested, the finish surface will not meet the installation standards for the project *[the impact]*.

7.2 Do's & Don'ts of Writing to Inform

In helping others with their writing skills, I have found it helpful to compile a list of do's and don'ts that address most of the lessons that, if learned, will produce better quality writing. The following is my list of do's and don'ts to follow when writing to inform.

1. *Do*: Get to the point of the issue or problem quickly.

> *Sometimes saying less can be more effective.*

Writing about construction problems should not be done the same way you would tell a story. When you tell a story, it is important to lead up to the main event. You build the scene, describe the characters, and provide the motivation to draw your audience into the main plot and then to the final conclusion of the story.

In writing about construction issues you should focus on the issue or problem as soon as possible. This type of writing is efficient and straight-forward. You should resist the tendency to give a long history of how the situation or problem evolved. If you have been diligent about documenting the problem as it evolved and feel that it is relevant to the issue, you could simply refer to your prior correspondence and other documents that would inform the reader in case they are interested (you can also attach them to your document). Although the reasons why the problem exists may be important for determining who may be responsible, sometimes that is not as easy to determine. Besides, if the focus of attention becomes "the cause" of the problem, that could paralyze the parties, resulting in greater expense and time to identify and implement a solution. Sometimes saying less is more effective.

2. **<u>Do</u>: Explain how the issue impacts your scope, cost, or time to perform.**

In the vast majority of cases the issues that arise during construction have to do with changes in project conditions that will impact your cost or time to perform. For this reason, the purpose of your writing will be two-fold:

   a. to describe the condition that exists, demonstrating how it differs from the plan or from what was anticipated, and

   b. to explain how this condition will impact your work by increasing your cost or extending the time for performance.

This simple, two-step formula for writing about issues will give you a template which you can use for the majority of your project correspondence.

3. **<u>Do: Stick to the facts.</u>**

I'm sure there have been times that, as you were describing an incident, you realized that you were missing some facts or details in order to make the picture complete. Like most people in this situation, you probably made up or assumed the missing facts to make your story work. While that may be accepted practice for some, and may not have repercussions in casual conversation among friends, that sort of practice can be dangerous if applied to your communications in construction.

We all want to sound like we know what we are saying. People also have a tendency to fill in the gaps and to offer as "fact" what many times is nothing more than an opinion or assumption. You should avoid doing this sort of thing in your communications. When we substitute opinions and assumptions for facts, we run the risk of distorting the record. If it turns out that our educated guesses were not true, then we could also end up losing credibility with others. In those cases where construction disputes arise and the issues must be decided by a third party (e.g. in arbitration or a court of law), the loss of credibility will be damaging to your cause.

Stick to the facts in your writing at all times, don't try to appear wiser than you are by offering "facts" of which you are not certain or have yet confirmed. If you think you need to offer an "educated guess" or an opinion, then present it as such, being careful not to offer it a as "fact".

4. *Don't: drown the reader in details or provide extraneous information.*

When writing about a problem or issue, you should offer enough background information to provide context, but be careful you don't go overboard. Providing an overabundance of detail and extraneous information can obscure the message and confuse the reader. In order to understand the issue being discussed, it is necessary for us to use the information and details provided by the writer. However, when the information serves no real purpose, it only muddles the message, leading to confusion and frustration.

You should avoid including extra information in correspondence, especially if it is not needed to understand the problem being discussed.

5. <u>**Do: include photographs where appropriate to avoid having to describe in lengthy detail what is visible in a picture.**</u>

We have heard it said many times, "a picture is worth a thousand words". Well, that can be true, provided, that is, that the picture is taken correctly and that the problem is one that will be visible in a photograph. I have seen many pictures that were supposed to demonstrate a problem condition which only ended up confusing me, leaving me with questions instead of information. Some problems do not lend themselves to pictures, so don't force the issue.

If you decide to take photographs of a problem, there are several things you can do to make sure that the result will inform the viewer of the condition you are noting.

a) If the condition is small, take a close up shot so that it will be visible (in addition to a longer view for orientation).

b) When there is poor lighting, make sure that you use a flash.

c) If there is little contrast, try looking at different angles to see if the condition shows up better.

d) Use a pencil or a pointer in the picture to identify the particular problem (if small) and to give a sense of scale.

e) Take a second picture of a similar setting where the problem doesn't exist to contrast the difference.

f) Finally, make sure that you describe what it is that the viewer should be looking for in the pictures you provide with your correspondence.

6. <u>**Do: consider including a possible solution to the problem.**</u>

I always found it constructive, whenever I wrote about problems in the past, to include a possible solution to the problem if I had identified one. I found that others appreciated this gesture and that many times they even adopted my suggested solution to the problem.

By offering constructive solutions, you are doing your best to be a team player. In addition, when you are faced with a problem for which alternative approaches could be taken to resolve it, your recommendation may be given greater weight than that of others who are less involved in the situation or have less at stake. It makes sense to offer solutions along with the problem when it's identified.

Finally, even if your proposed solution is not adopted, over time you should be seen as someone that others would want to have on their team, since you are not just someone that points out the problems, but offers their solutions as well.

CHAPTER EIGHT

Being Clear when Communicating

P P R I <u>C</u> K

In the last chapter I spent some time on ways to improve your writing to inform others, since most project correspondence is for the purpose of conveying information.

Considering the subject of communications in general now, I would like to ask a couple of questions. What is the best way to communicate when working on construction projects? Is there an easy way to learn how to write about construction problems?

As someone who has spent his career focusing on construction issues and their solution, I have been deeply involved in all manner of documentation when it comes to construction situations and problems. I will attempt to answer these questions here. As you follow along, keep in mind that although I am focusing on written communication (e.g. emails and letters), the basic principles I discuss apply to your spoken communications as well.

8.1 Why You Need to be Clear

Commercial construction projects can be complex and expensive undertakings. They are usually financed by third parties and therefore a great deal of value/weight will be placed on misunderstandings, mistakes, and delays. The pace of work can be fast and furious too. These and other factors create an environment where the communication of problems can be charged with emotion and urgency.

Given these concerns, my single most important advice when it comes to communications is to be clear. Your goal each time you communicate should be to let your writing and discussions leave no question about what you are saying.

Once again, I will offer my do's and don'ts to help you with your writing.

8.2 Do's & Don'ts

Rather than boring you with detailed rules on grammar and sentence structure (which I also hated when they were being taught in school), I think it's best to jump right into some basic rules that I have assembled to help you achieve clarity in your writing.

While following these rules will not make you a Shakespeare or Frost, that is not the purpose of this manual. My goal (and yours) is to improve the way you write. To do that, I need to strip away many bad habits that you may be carrying around which have made your communication sloppy, confusing, and difficult to understand. These may be some of the same reasons that you find writing to be difficult and a burden for you. So let's get started.

1. ***Don't:*** **try to impress with your writing.**

   Some people seem to think that when they communicate in writing they need to do so in a manner that they would never use when speaking. They try to write in a way that is unnatural for them, in a style which they have no business using for construction matters.

   Perhaps it's the fact that since they are doing something they seldom do (writing a formal letter or email about a serious topic) they believe they need to write it like their lawyer would draft a lawsuit. There are two problems with that approach; 1) they are not lawyers, and 2) these are not situations that require a legal style of writing. To make matters worse, these are usually the same contractors that tell me they prefer not to document issues because they don't wish to escalate problems by writing letters. If you could step back from the problem, you should be able to see why this type of writing is confusing, threatening, and will tend to upset the reader without providing much clarity. This style of writing is what often results with someone getting labeled a "PRICK". That is what we are trying to avoid!

When you write about construction issues you should not be trying to impress anyone with your writing abilities. Your main purpose is to communicate clearly and without any ambiguity so that the reader knows exactly what you are saying, and why. If you want to impress folks with your writing, learn to write poetry or novels as a hobby.

2. *Do: simplify your writing.*

> *Simplicity is the glory of expression.*
> *(Walt Whitman)*

Shorter sentences are best – one thought at a time! If you have difficulty writing, or if you find that people are confused with what you are trying to communicate, this is probably the best way to build your confidence. By following this rule to keep your sentences short and deal with only one thought at a time, chances are you will avoid many common writing mistakes. You will be more likely to communicate your message with clarity.

It takes more effort to write using compound sentences that deal with multiple or interrelated thoughts. It's perfectly okay to write in short sentences that contain one subject or thought at a time. That makes it easy for the reader to piece together the thoughts and understand the entire message without confusion. In fact, as a reader, I would prefer that approach over having to fight my way through a series of convoluted thoughts that may not be put together properly and could be interpreted with various meanings.

3. *Do: stick to familiar words.*

Perhaps also in an effort to impress others with their writing, I often find the inclusion of many words in construction correspondence which the writer used incorrectly. In fact, sometimes the words used convey the opposite meaning than that which was intended by the writer. This careless practice not only results in confusion, but it can also be dangerous when dealing with important issues. In addition, instead of leaving a good impression with the reader, it could make the writer look foolish or ignorant.

If you are not sure about the meaning of words that you want to include in your writing look them up. Aside from laziness, there is no excuse today when most software programs include built-in dictionaries and online resources are also available on demand for free.

4. *Don't: beat around the bush, don't imply.*

Nothing can be more frustrating than having to read a long letter from someone and, having reached the end of the letter, asking yourself "what was the writer trying to tell me, what was the purpose of this letter?" The construction business is heavy in facts and details, one can easily get sidetracked and end up not describing the main point, when trying to communicate an issue.

In addition, when the subject that needs to be communicated is a serious problem which could be controversial, there is a tendency to try to mask the issue or to dance around it without getting directly to the point in an effort to "soften the blow". I find that most people would rather be told about a serious problem up front without "beating around the bush". If time is money, the sooner a problem can be identified, understood, addressed, and resolved, the better it will be for the project participants.

I should make one more comment about this – if your communication is required by contract (e.g. a notice that must be served on the other party), you should not want to leave any doubt that you complied with the contract and therefore you should be very direct in your writing. However, that does not mean you should be angry or offensive in your writing.

5. <u>*Don't: repeat yourself, be redundant, or say things twice...*</u>

I am sure you know some people who give the impression that they like to hear themselves talk. If you are like me, you probably find that having a conversation with this type of person is very annoying and you tend to avoid them if possible. Since writing is really another form of expression, I am fairly certain that this type of person cannot keep their writing short. A common way used to lengthen their writing is by repetition, the same way they would ramble on in a conversation.

Construction correspondence is one type of business writing. As with all business writing, it is good practice to avoid being repetitious which can be viewed as a form of inefficiency. It is one thing to repeat a point to give added emphasis of its importance. However, to say the same thing in different ways over and over is just boring and a bad practice. It requires the reader to waste valuable time and can even distract the reader from the intended message.

Remember, business correspondence is not like writing an essay for school, there is no requirement for you to make your writing a certain fixed length. I have been most impressed when I have come across writing that conveyed a very clear meaning on an important issue in one or two simple sentences. That is effective writing!

6. <u>*Don't: use personal criticism or attack, sarcasm, profanity, exaggeration, boasting, flowery writing, double meanings, or jokes.*</u>

Your business writing should not reflect the way you might think or speak in the heat of an argument. If that is a tendency you have, you should wait until you calm down before you write. While it is usually unproductive to fly off the handle at someone over an issue, when done in writing, you leave a permanent record that can be very damaging and difficult to reverse. This type of damage could have a lasting effect.

When you stop to think about it, using personal attacks, sarcasm, or profanity in your writing is disrespectful and can be hurtful. Regardless of how you may feel about the person you are writing to, you will agree that personalizing an argument does not advance the understanding of a problem or the solution of a dispute. In fact, it will only serve to escalate the disagreement to a higher level which will most likely guarantee it will not be resolved without both sides having to spend more time and money. Once again, that is something that you should be trying to avoid since it won't be helpful to your bottom line on the project.

If you must be critical, stick to criticizing the actions, decisions, or circumstances and not the individual. Instead of expressing your anger, provide an explanation of the anticipated damage that may result from the problem or circumstances which have been created.

I always found it helpful to write a draft of any important message and go back to it after a while to re-read it. In nearly all cases, upon re-reading it, I have found that there was a better way to make my point, without personalizing an issue. I highly recommend this practice. In addition, it can be helpful to have someone else in your company read your draft; someone who is not emotionally invested in the issue like you might be.

Exaggeration and boasting will distort the facts in the record and may cause you to appear dishonest or untrustworthy at a later point in time. Remember, your credibility is extremely important. What you put in writing should stand the test of time and the facts (if not in the eyes of your reader, in the eyes of an impartial, unbiased observer who may be deciding later on who was "right" in your dispute).

As I mentioned before, flowery writing doesn't have a place in construction correspondence. Similarly, the use of double meanings and jokes in your writing can have unintended consequences.

You should avoid creating confusion or doubts about your message; stick to the facts and to the intended purpose of your message, be clear.

7. *Do: think before you write.*

> *Writing is thinking.*

I was first exposed to this concept by a good friend, who I consider to be an excellent writer. He explained to me how most of the problems that are attributed to poor writing result from the failure to think before writing. Whenever you start to write, it is crucial to take the time to gather your thoughts.

If your writing is confusing, long-winded, disjointed or otherwise poor, the chances are you are not taking the time to think before you write. Your writing is merely reactionary; you may be writing off the "top of your head" which may be the source of all of your problems.

If you are confused in your mind about how to approach an issue but begin to write about it nonetheless, your writing will be a reflection of your confused thinking and will not be clear or easy to follow.

If you lack complete understanding of a problem, it will be a challenge for you to describe the nature or origin of the problem, and even more so, to identify the best possible solution.

By now, I think you can see how good writing necessarily flows from proper thinking. When you stop to "think" about this, it just makes perfect sense!

So how should you approach writing? If you follow the steps below I think you will have a great start:

1. Think before you write. Take the time to gather your thoughts.

2. Think about the issue or problem from as many angles as possible. Don't assume your initial understanding of the problem is always correct.

3. If you don't understand something or don't know a key fact, get the information that will complete your understanding.

4. Do not write while angry or emotional.

5. Make a simple outline of the key points that you wish to communicate before you start the actual message. Stick to the "what" and "why" formula for your message.

6. Compose a draft of your message from your outline.

7. Review and edit your draft message (for important correspondence, have someone else edit too if possible).

CHAPTER NINE

Summary

BE A **"PPRICK"**

Perform

be **P**roactive

be **R**esponsive

write to **I**nform

be **C**lear when communicating

Know your contract

9.1 *Putting it all Together*

In the last two chapters I explained how your writing should strive for clarity and be focused on performance with the goal of informing the reader about the situations and problems you want to communicate. We also went through many practical tips to help you prepare more effective correspondence through the do's and don'ts that were presented.

In this chapter I will put it all together in a couple of case studies that should be familiar territory to anyone that has worked in construction. However, before I take you through the case studies, I think it is important to go through an example of a poorly written letter to review the mistakes that are often made. The letter below, though fictitious, could have been real. Unfortunately, I have seen many like it before. It is from a subcontractor writing to a general contractor to complain about a situation that has developed on a project.

Dear GC,

At this point in time, it has come to my attention that there may be a problem in so far as our work schedule is concerned, something that we talked about last week during our job meeting but something which we have not had the occasion to go over in detail. I believe that this problem may have been related to the numerous, and enormous changes that were originally made to the foundations by the structural engineer which we had told you about early during one of the project meetings but which we noticed today you did not record (as usual) in the official minutes of the meetings that were distributed.

The subject of my concern (which is what caused our blow up at the current meeting when I caught you lying about your comments) is that several of the other trades are being told over and over that they need to come in on Saturdays to work on the interior bathroom rough-ins for the first floor because the work is now about 4 weeks behind the latest version of the schedule which you issued about 2 months ago, irregardless of the fact that you did not issue us a Change Order to cover the cost of our proposal for the extra cost of that overtime that was necessary.

Therefore, we do not believe that it is good practice or fair when I remember what you told the mechanical superintendent at last week's meeting about working without pay, that we should continue to agree to your ridiculous demands to meet the new schedule deadlines that you are now saying for the first time that we must meet by your schedule update issued in February...

Are you dizzy yet? Frustrated? Like me, you may have obtained a general sense of what the writer was trying to communicate, but getting through this letter felt like hard labor. Having reached the end, you probably asked yourself: "exactly what was the point of the letter?"

Let's review the problems first, before I offer a more effective solution.

1. The most obvious problem was the long, compound sentences that were poorly constructed.

2. Next was the overabundance of details and unrelated comments that were included which had very little to do with the problem. The writer did not stick to the facts.

3. You also could say that the writer was exaggerating, used personal criticism and was repetitious.

4. There was no objectivity in the letter and plenty of subjective comments and opinions offered.

5. There was the use of the word "irregardless" which has no meaning. I realize that this is often incorrectly substituted for "regardless" by many, but it is a mistake nonetheless.

6. The writer did not get to the problem quickly. In fact, the entire first paragraph was a prelude that went nowhere. The delays in the foundation may have been important in the past, but there was no direct link provided to the current problem being discussed.

7. The letter did not clearly set forth the problem or issue, nor did it describe the impact to the scope, cost or time of performance.

8. Finally, the letter was full of criticism, and empty of solutions.

9. It is obvious that the writer did not gather his thoughts before writing this letter.

Now let's see how we can improve on this communication. I will do this exercise one paragraph at a time. As an alternative to the introductory paragraph, I suggest:

> *The delays in the foundations have caused other follow-on work on this project to be delayed. We brought this to your attention during Progress Meeting #12 (a copy of our letter correcting the minutes of that meeting is attached).*

This provides a clean introduction and links the fact that the project delays in the past are the cause of the current problems. Notice the use of separate, shorter sentences that express each thought. Of course, I have altered the facts to show that the writer had actually written to correct the minutes of the prior meeting in which he had brought up the delays during the progress meeting (something that is good practice).

The real point of the message is now simplified in the suggested second paragraph as follows:

> *Other trades are working on Saturdays on the interior bathroom rough-ins for the first floor in order to make up the delay. We issued our proposal to you for the added cost of this overtime but have not received a Change Order or any direction in accordance with our contract.*

Note how all of the extraneous information and personal references have been removed. The letter now reports on the facts, rather than the "he said-she said" dialog employed in the original. Additionally, there is now a direct reference to the contract which is necessary.

The final paragraph has been reduced to a short sentence:

> *If you would like for us to work on Saturdays we will require written direction from you in accordance with our contract.*

This last paragraph, which could be combined with the second, is unambiguous, direct, and based on the contract terms.

Please note that the revised letter is now less than half as long as the original, however, it provides the reader with the proper context, it contains a clear message and is focused on the facts and the impact of the problem. The suggested solution is also included.

9.2 Case Study 1: Extra Work

Background:

The need for most construction documentation arises from one of two causes; disagreements over extra work, or delays. In this section I will take you through a sample request for extra work and analyze the typical trail of correspondence that takes place between two parties as they deal with this issue. My sample correspondence is designed to be a dialog between a general contractor and an architect. Throughout this exercise I will highlight the problems that should be avoided as well as the good practices that should be followed. The case study should serve as a good example of the "PPRICK" principles at work.

As in all cases of alleged discrepancies in the scope of work, it is necessary for the contractor to demonstrate how the actual field conditions differ from what is shown in the Contract Documents. This is usually accomplished through a comparison of the applicable sections of those documents with the description of the field conditions (dimensions, photos, etc.). The inclusions of references to codes and standards which may factor in the conflict are also pointed out.

The correspondence in these cases will necessarily include excerpts from, references to, or copies of the contract drawings, specifications, special conditions, contract articles, and applicable code sections. This is done to facilitate the communication of the problem and to allow the reader to see more clearly the conflict that is the subject of the alleged extra work.

For our purposes, let's assume the following situation; the Contract Documents give a dimension for the mechanical closets in the hallways of a condominium building that does not allow enough room for the mechanical and electrical equipment according to the applicable codes.

Applying what we have learned, the contractor is required to give notice of this conflict within a certain period of time after he first becomes aware of it according to the contract. In this case, the contract might read:

"Any design errors or omissions noted by the Contractor during this review shall be reported promptly to the Architect..."

Round 1 (identification of the problem):

So, the first correspondence on this issue is written by our contractor (Mr. P.Prick) to the architect (Mr. Prick) as follows:

Dear Mr. Prick / Architect,

We have just completed our coordination review of the mechanical and electrical shop drawings for the equipment closets in the typical hallways (coordination drawing and submittals attached). It appears that there was not enough room allowed in the design to accommodate the specified equipment and allow the working clearances required by Code (attached are the pertinent Contract Document references and Code sections).

We have met with the subcontractors involved and have come up with what we believe will be the best workable solution to this problem, involving the least amount of change to the existing work that is in place. We are providing you with our proposal for this solution and the associated costs for your review and approval.

Sincerely,
Mr. P.Prick / Contractor

You will note that our contractor has done a good job of staying focused on the facts in his communication. His letter was direct, informing and clearly identified the problem. The letter did not include any personal attacks, it was quite professional. In addition, in an effort to assist the architect, our contractor included a proactive suggestion for solving the problem. This letter is a fine example of the application of many of the good practices we discussed in earlier chapters.

There are two types of objections that cause extra work disputes;

1. objection over price
2. objection over entitlement

I will deal with them in that order.

Round 1 (rejection – objection over price):

Continuing with our case study, the architect's responses to our contractor will contain many of the pitfalls that we have previously discussed, and that you should take care to avoid. The architect's initial rejection follows:

> *Dear Mr. P.Prick,*
>
> *I have reviewed your submission concerning the design of the mechanical closets. Your price is rejected, and I believe it is extremely high to the point that it looks like you are trying to take advantage of the situation. It looks like your subcontractors have used unrealistically high labor units and material prices which are not applicable to this work. Please revise your submission using standard labor units and re-submit.*
>
> *In addition, you have used the wrong mark-up (you apparently ignored the contract which limits your total markup to ___% for the allowable cost categories for changes).*
>
> *You need to revise and resubmit your request as soon as possible to avoid delay.*
>
> *Sincerely,*
> *Mr. Prick*

The architect was obviously having a bad day and chose to personalize the issue, used inflammatory remarks and took a confrontational position with our contractor.

Round 2 (resubmission and correction):

Our contractor believes in the PPRICK principles and does not follow the architect down the path of personalizing the issue or taking a confrontational approach. Instead, noticing that the architect was correct in his objection to the mark-up that was used in the initial proposal pricing, he corrects his mistake and resubmits the request for extra as follows:

> *Mr. Prick,*
>
> *Enclosed please find our resubmission of the Change Order for the additional work to have the mechanical closets conform to Code.*
>
> *We have re-priced the work to reflect the allowed mark-up on changes per the contract. However, we believe we have used correct labor units and respectfully disagree with you.*
>
> *We request a meeting with you and the Owner as soon as possible in order to resolve this matter.*

Our contractor has taken the high road. In correcting his mistake he is now standing on firm ground to pursue his request confidently. Many times, when confronted with an error in the calculation of change requests, I have seen contractors stick to their guns with the errors, thinking that by so doing, they will have something with which to bargain when the time comes for resolution of the dispute. On the contrary, this will work against them every single time, since it makes them appear ignorant, at best, and untrustworthy at worst. In my experience, contractors who practice this tactic will find that all future change requests are scrutinized even more severely as a result.

Resolution of Dispute:

In the time between our contractor's resubmission and the architect's response, a meeting with the owner has taken place and it was decided that the disputed extra work should commence. The architect responded as follows:

> *Dear Mr. P.Prick,*
>
> *As a follow-up to our recent meeting, we are providing you herewith with a Change Order to proceed with the work on the mechanical closets.*

You will note that since we disagree on the price, the CO states "price to be determined".

Please proceed immediately with this change as required by the contract. You are also warned not to bill any more than explicitly allowed by the contract!

Since the contract allowed for time and material billing in the event that no agreement could be reached on price, the work proceeded in accordance with the contract. No further response was necessary on the part of our contractor. Although in many real-life cases the resolution of extra work disputes may take longer, requiring more re-submissions, the purpose of this case study is to demonstrate the way that correspondence should be handled between the parties.

Round 1 Alternate (rejection – objection over entitlement):

We go back now to the initial response from the architect to our contractor's submission of the extra work request and assume, instead, that the objection was over entitlement to the extra work (i.e. there is a question as to whether the work is part of the original scope of the contract).

Dear Mr. P.Prick,

Your requested extra work is rejected, we believe the work is shown on the Contract Documents (drawings A101, note 4 and specification sections ####).

In addition, we need to point out that any minor omissions in our design that arise from coordination of the work are contemplated in the Contract (see article ___ for minor omissions in the drawings). You should have known that this work was therefore in your scope and is not an extra.

Please proceed with the work without further delay, and in the future we hope you won't submit any more needless claims for extras as it takes away from our time on more important matters. We reserve the right to charge you for our time reviewing future unfounded requests for extras.

Sincerely,
Mr. Prick

You will note that the architect has taken a confrontational approach and has resorted to attacks.

Round 2 (resubmission and demand):

Dear Mr. Prick,

We are resubmitting our request for change with all support documents. We disagree with your interpretation of our contract since we do not have design responsibility. Enclosed are several publications that are consistent with our view and confirm what the standard practice is in our industry.

We request a meeting including the Owner in order to resolve this matter. If you wish for us to proceed without a Change Order (as stated in your letter) kindly issue a written Directive in accordance with our contract. We will also need to have your approved revised drawing that incorporates the changes to the design of the mechanical closets so we can proceed with the work.

Here we can see how our contractor is applying the contract "rules" in his letter, making demand for a written directive and an approved revised drawing before being able to proceed with the disputed work. As in the case of the objection over price, our contractor requests a meeting with the owner in order to expedite the resolution of the dispute.

Round 2 (architect's response and directive to proceed):

Dear Mr. P.Prick,

We conducted our final review of your requested extra work and have decided that it was included in your contract scope as we determined initially. Your request is therefore rejected.

Enclosed is our Directive and a sketch with the minor changes required to the mechanical closets. Please proceed with this work as per the contract without further delay.

Sincerely,
Mr. Prick

Round 2 (contractor's response - notice of claim):

Based on the architect's response, our contractor has no choice but to proceed under protest. However, using the rules of the contract, he gives notice of his intent to file a claim for the extra work dispute.

Dear Mr. Prick,

Thank you for issuing your sketch for the revised design of the mechanical closets and your Directive for us to proceed.

We are proceeding under protest and will be submitting our claim for the additional cost associated with this work in accordance with our contract (Article ##).

Sincerely,
Mr. P.Prick

cc: Owner

As you can see, our contractor's letter gets to the point quickly, is professional and cordial. It is followed up in a timely manner with the claim as follows:

Dear Owner / Mr. Prick,

Enclosed please find our claim for the additional cost associated with the mechanical closet revisions. We are available to meet with you to resolve this matter amicably, after you have had the opportunity to review it.

Sincerely,
Mr. P.Prick

Our contractor continues to be non-confrontational in his documentation, despite the certain difficulty of having to perform the disputed work without compensation, pending the resolution of the dispute.

Since our contractor has read the contract, he is aware of the sequence and the timing of the steps that must be taken to resolve this dispute. He will wait the required time allowed by contract before filing the demand to commence the formal dispute resolution method prescribed in his contract.

9.3 Case Study 2: Delay

Background:

I mentioned earlier that most construction documents originate either from extra work situations, or a delay to the schedule. In this second case study, I will take you through an example involving a delay by studying the trail of correspondence that might typically take place during the life of this issue.

I have designed the correspondence in this case study to be a one way dialog form a mechanical subcontractor to a general contractor. This is due to the fact that the general contractor in this example is not very responsive. What response is made by him is addressed in my comments and assumptions. As in the prior case study on disputed extra work, I will highlight the problems that should be avoided as well as the good practices that should be followed. This case study is also intended to reinforce the "PPRICK" principles that are at work.

We start with the following assumptions:

1. The contract states that "time is of the essence" and includes liquidated damages for delay.
2. The foundations on the project are delayed due to unforeseen conditions (the foundation work is on the critical path).
3. The general contractor has failed to issue a revised schedule to show how the delay will be recovered.

Round 1 (identification of the problem):

Our mechanical subcontractor's project manager has learned to be proactive and knows the importance of documenting conditions that could potentially delay his work and hurt the profitability of his company on this project. He begins with the following letter to the general contractor:

Dear Mr. Prick,

Our company takes pride in planning our work so that we can serve you by completing our activities in accordance with the schedule. The project schedule calls for our underground plumbing work to start next week (activity 1501).

Currently it looks like the installation of the foundations which precede our work will not be complete in time to allow us to start on schedule. Please let us know if we should revise the planned start date for our work. Also, please allow this to serve as our notice of delay as required by our subcontract in the event we are unable to start as planned.

Notice the following good practices employed by our subcontractor in this letter:

- The letter is performance focused
- It conveys a cooperative spirit
- It gives the general contractor time to make adjustments
- Serves as a proactive notice of delay
- The message is clear and informing

Assume now the following additional facts:

1. The general contractor did not respond to the notice of delay from the mechanical subcontractor. The lack of response to an important issue is not a good practice on the part of a contractor.

2. The mechanical contractor is finally able to start 3 weeks later than planned, since the foundation conflict took longer to resolve.

3. Underground plumbing work is now projected to complete 4 weeks late due to additional weather delays.

Round 2 (continuing notice and update of issue):

Based on these additional facts, the following correspondence should be submitted by our mechanical subcontractor:

Dear Mr. Prick,

As a follow-up to our prior notice, we were able to start our underground plumbing work on February 18, three weeks later than planned due to the foundation delays.

We anticipate being complete with that work by April 2nd, about 4 weeks behind the project schedule due to the late start and the rain delays that took place during the past two weeks (see Daily Reports attached).

It would be beneficial for us to have a revised schedule for the remainder of the work, since the delays are making it difficult to plan our work, and we notice that some contractors are starting to work out of sequence in portions of the project.

Please let us know if you would like our input to revise the schedule.

Once again, notice the following good practices employed by our subcontractor in the second letter:

- The letter is performance focused
- It gives the general contractor time to make adjustments
- It conveys a cooperative spirit (offers to assist with revised schedule)
- Serves as a continuing notice of delay
- The message is clear and informing

Again, let's assume some additional facts take place:

1. Mr. Prick (the GC) responded to the 2nd notice of delay from Mr. P.Prick (our mechanical subcontractor), stating that the delays were minor, and he would be revising the schedule to show how the project could still be completed on time. This projection is unrealistic, of course, failing to reflect the reality of the situation that has evolved on the project.

2. In the meantime, progress has been made, but not without additional problems: the mason lacked

manpower and was delaying the start of interiors, also the core area of the building had to be re-designed to meet building Codes.

Round 3 (continuing delays, notice of claim):

Based on these additional developments, the following correspondence is recommended as appropriate under the circumstances for our mechanical subcontractor:

> *Dear Mr. Prick,*
>
> *It has been months since we requested a revised schedule – we really believe it is necessary. We have only been able to install our interior rough-ins in bits and pieces due to the lack of areas that have masonry completed, and the re-design of the core area which has caused all work to stop in the building core.*
>
> *Given the fact that we are working piece meal throughout the project and that work is now taking place out of sequence due to the numerous areas on hold, the progress of our work is being delayed on a daily basis.*
>
> *Please consider this as our notice of continuing delay under our contract. We are currently unable to determine the extent of delay, due to the lack of existence of a workable project schedule. We reserve all of our rights under the contract. Be advised that we will submit our claim to request the additional time and cost once we are able to determine the impact.*

Once again, notice the following good practices employed by our subcontractor in this second letter:

- The letter is performance focused
- It gives the general contractor time to make adjustments
- Serves as a continuing notice of delay
- The letter provided a notice of claim according to contract

- The message is clear and informing
- Though the letter is direct, the tone is non-confrontational

Again, let's continue with more assumed events and the following additional facts in our case:

1. Seeing that the mechanical subcontractor has now mentioned that a claim will be prepared for the delays, the general contractor (Mr. Prick) responded to the prior letter from Mr. P.Prick, objecting to the notice of claim, stating that every subcontractor had contributed to the delays (without giving any support). He requested a revised schedule for the remainder of the work from Mr. P.Prick and insisted that it show the project completing on schedule, reminding him that there will be liquidated damages to pay otherwise.

2. In the meantime, the work on the project had become more disorganized and the original project schedule was abandoned in favor of hastily prepared look-ahead schedules provided in the progress meetings (done without subcontractor input).

Round 4 (response to GC's threats of liquidated damages):

Based on the latest developments, it would be easy for our subcontractor to get upset and allow his communication to be dictated by the absurdity of the general contractor's statements. However, our subcontractor takes the proper, professional approach in his response as follows:

Dear Mr. Prick,

We are now 10 months into construction and have only completed about 4 months of work according to our original schedule. The project needs to be brought under control. We need decisions made to release areas on hold, critical activities that are lagging need to be made current and a revised schedule needs to be created to guide the work towards an orderly completion.

We share your frustration, but disagree with your statements about our company being partly to blame for the delays. The record reflects that we have been unable to start our work on critical activities. We have also been forced to work in a piece meal, fragmented manner, without logical sequence which has reduced our productivity throughout. We have provided you with notice of these events from the beginning of the problems (a copy of our prior correspondence is attached).

Our company stands willing to work with you and to cooperate under the terms of our subcontract to help you bring this project to completion as soon as possible. However, we will defend against any attempt to hold us accountable for the actions or inactions of others.

Rather than taking the inaccurate remarks of the GC personal, our subcontractor refutes them with the facts. In addition, the message in this letter demonstrates the following good practices:

- The letter is performance focused
- The message is clear and informing
- Serves as a continuing notice of delay
- The letter evidences a continued cooperative spirit
- Though very direct, the tone of the letter is non-confrontational

Finally, we continue our case with the following assumptions:

1. Mr. Prick did not respond to the prior letter from Mr. P.Prick.

2. Work on the project continued with great difficulty. As the original completion date approached Mr. P.Prick was able to compile sufficient cost data to prepare his company's claim.

Round 5 (delay claim submitted):

> *Dear Mr. Prick,*
>
> *Pursuant to our prior notice of claim, enclosed please find our claim for the additional costs to date and our projected additional costs to complete. Our claim also requests an extension of time of ___ days.*
>
> *Our claim addresses the additional costs that have resulted from the delays to our work, the reduced productivity caused by the severe disruption from all of the work stoppages and fragmented availability of the work areas. In addition, we are presenting our costs for the additional supervision and project administrative costs that have been incurred (and are projected to completion) due to these problems.*
>
> *This claim is based on the current projected completion date for our work which we forecast to be _____. We have included many attachments to our claim that support our entitlement and the amount of our calculations. We reserve our right to amend this claim for any events that arise between now and the completion of the project. We look forward to a constructive resolution of this claim and are ready to meet with you after you have reviewed our claim.*

Our subcontractor has followed up the notice of claim with a submission of his claim as soon as he was able to determine the amount of the impact. In this case, as the work is still not complete, he has made allowances for the anticipated completion date and has reserved his right to make changes when the work is completed. I think you will agree that his style was consistent with his prior communication and that this letter provides the following:

- A clear and informing message
- Submission of the claim for which notice had been provided

- The letter evidences a continued cooperative spirit
- Though very direct, the tone of the letter is non-confrontational

From this point on, the situation will probably be one that is handled under the guidance of the subcontractor's attorney. Depending on the options provided in the contract, this dispute, if not resolved through a negotiated settlement will need to proceed with either arbitration or litigation.

However, the advantage that the subcontractor has is that by submitting his claim during the project instead of waiting until the end, there is a greater awareness of this issue which in my experience improves the chances for a continuing dialog, opening up the possibility of and earlier settlement of the dispute, than if he had waited until the completion of the project.

9.4 Applying the "PPRICK" Principles to Your Projects

I hope that I have been able to provide you with a solid framework of principles you can use to help you manage your construction projects. I also hope that you have acquired a better appreciation for the reasons why documenting your project issues in accordance with the contract will help to reduce the risk that you will end up with greater costs and less profit. As with all new things that are learned, application and repetition are the keys to achieving the desired results. It is not enough to learn a new approach, you must act on it!

It is normal for you to feel uncomfortable when first applying a new way of doing something that is different from the way you've done it in the past. That is why it may be necessary to refer back to sections of this manual to remind you of the approach that is called for to document various conditions. In addition, in order for a new management approach to take hold firmly in an organization, it needs to be promoted from the top of the organization and encouraged periodically.

It is my hope that with the proper discipline, as you apply these principles repetitively, through habit, they will become an integral part of the management process on all of your projects. You will see that it is not necessary to be confrontational or antagonistic when corresponding with others about difficult issues in order to get results. Over time, you will also discover that creating effective written communication is not as difficult as it once seemed. To assist you in preparing your communications, I have prepared many sample paragraphs that address numerous typical project conditions which require documentation. Feel free to use these as a starting point to generate your own correspondence as your circumstances may require.

It is my firm belief that the consistent application of these principles will assist you in managing the many issues and problems encountered on construction projects. As a result of their application, they will reduce your risk and increase your profit.

As I close this instruction manual, I leave you with one of my favorite quotes which describes what I believe is necessary to make these principles work.

> ***We are what we repeatedly do.***
> ***Excellence, then, is not an act, but a habit.***
> *(Aristotle)*

Make it your goal to be excellent when managing your construction projects, be a *"PPRICK"*, without being a PRICK!

APPENDIX A:

CONTRACT "RULES" CHECKLIST

As an owner of this manual, you can download a copy of this form (in Microsoft Word file format) from my resource website: **www.constructionletters.com.**

Document to Reduce Risk

Contract "Rules" Checklist

Project: _____   by: _____

Project Stage & Subject	Clauses in Contract	Clauses in Other Docs.	Written Notice?	Days to Notify	Who Gives Authority?	Notes / Comments
Notice						
PRE-CONSTRUCTION / MOBILIZATION						
Shop Drawings						
Substitutions						
Samples						
Temporary Facilities						
Hours of Work						
Attendance at Meetings						
Daily Reports						
PERFORMANCE						
Drawings & Specifications						
Labor Force						
Materials & Workmanship						
Work Methods						
Protection						
Cutting & Patching						
Cleaning-up						
COORDINATION & SEQUENCE						
Coordination & Cooperation						
Materials Furn. by Others						
Separate Contractors						
PAYMENT						
Payments (progress)						
Stored Materials						
Retainage						
Non-Payment						
Interest on Payment						
CHANGES						
Change Orders						
Cost & Pricing Changes						
Differing (concealed) Conditions						
Change Directives						
TIME, SCHEDULE, DELAY						
Time (completion)						
Progress Schedules						
Interference & Obstructions						
Time Extension						
Acceleration						
Suspension of Work						
DAMAGES FOR DELAY						
Liquidated Damages						
Damages for Delay						

construction management form design by **Farach Consultants, Inc.**

Contract "Rules" Checklist

Project: _____   by: _____

Project Stage & Subject	Clauses in Contract	Clauses in Other Docs.	Written Notice?	Days to Notify	Who Gives Authority?	Notes / Comments
CLAIMS						
Claims, Disputes						
Damages						
Equitable Adjustment						
Termination (for convenience)						
RESOLUTION OF CLAIMS & DISPUTES						
Mediation of Disputes						
Arbitration of Disputes						
Trial						
Venue						
FAILURE TO PERFORM / TERMINATION						
Non-conforming Work						
Uncovering & Correction						
Rejection of Work						
Cure Period						
Supplementing Labor						
Termination (for cause)						
GENERAL						
Insurance						
Indemnification						
Permits & Licenses						
Bond						
Subcontracts						
CLOSE-OUT						
Punch List						
Final Inspection & Tests						
Inspection & Acceptance						
Substantial Completion						
Partial (beneficial) Occupancy						
Cost Accounting & Audits						

construction management form design by **_Farach Consultants, Inc._**

APPENDIX B:

SAMPLE LETTERS

As an owner of this manual, you can download a copy of the sample letters in this appendix (in Microsoft Word file format) from my resource website: **www.constructionletters.com.**

The language in these samples is offered as practical suggestions to assist managers in documenting the events and issues that typically arise during the construction process. Some communications such as reservation of rights, payment disputes, and positions on claims may be critical and should be considered carefully. The user is strongly encouraged to solicit the advice of a competent attorney prior to issuing critical communications.

1. Pre-Construction & Mobilization

1.1 Contract Documents

1.1.1 Request for missing Contract Documents

<u>Keys</u>:

- Do this before executing the contract.

<u>Caution</u>:

- Consult with your attorney prior to executing contract.

    In reviewing the contract for [insert project name] which you sent to us for execution, we note that the following Contract Documents are missing:

    - *[list the missing documents using the titles given in the contract]*

    Kindly provide us with these documents at your earliest convenience so we may be able to complete our review and execute the contract.   [1.1.1]

1.1.2 Contract Documents don't match the bid documents

<u>Keys</u>:

- Do this before executing the contract.
- Make sure all versions of Contract Documents match the ones used in preparing your bid.

<u>Caution</u>:

- Consult with your attorney prior to executing contract.

    In reviewing the contract for [insert project name] which you sent to us for execution, we note that the following Contract Documents are different than the ones which were used for our bid:

    - *[list the documents in question and the version (and date) provided versus the version (and date) used in the bid]*

Please let us know if you would like for us to provide you with a summary of the changes between these documents and the cost difference, if any. We will be unable to execute our contract until we can reconcile these changed documents with you.

[1.1.2]

1.2 Shop Drawings & Other Submittals

Most projects will have established specific transmittal forms for the submission of materials and equipment to the design professionals for their review and approval. The sample language below can usually be included within these forms, or can be used to create a new form in the event that one is not provided. Another option is to include this language in the body of an email or other correspondence that attaches the transmittal form.

1.2.1 Transmittal of shop drawings (or other submittals)

Keys:

- Review the contract and specifications to identify all materials and products that are required to be submitted to the design professionals for approval.
- Prepare a transmittal log that includes all of these materials and products.
- Consult the project schedule to identify the key work activities that are dependent on the return of product submittals for materials and equipment.
- Prepare your submissions of shop drawings timely, allowing sufficient time for review, so that your work is not delayed.
- Check with the contract to make sure that your requested date of return is not less than the minimum time allowed for review by the design professionals.
- Include all required information with each submittal in accordance with the requirements in the contract.

- Note in the transmittal log the dates by which the submittals are required to be returned and set up calendar reminders for follow up.

  Enclosed please find the following submittals for your review and approval on this project in accordance with our contract:

  - *[list the product description for the materials and equipment being submitted, the corresponding specification section, and the date by which the response is needed]*

  We will need these product submittals reviewed and returned to us by the dates noted above in order to be able to continue with our work in accordance with the project schedule.   [1.2.1]

1.2.2 Shop drawings (or other submittals) response needed

Keys:

- Use reminder system set up in 1.2.1 to trigger the follow-up correspondence, ideally sent a few days before the response is due.

  This is to inform you that we have not yet received a response to the submittals of materials/equipment which were sent to you as follows:

  - *[list the product description for the materials and equipment that were submitted, the specification section, and the date by which the response was due]*

  We need to have these submittals returned by the dates above in order to avoid a delay to our work according to the project schedule.   [1.2.2]

1.2.3 Shop drawings (or other submittals) delayed,   work impacted

Keys:

- Review the contract to obtain the notice requirements for delays.

  This is to inform you that we have not yet received a response to the submittals of materials/equipment which were sent to you on the following dates:

  - *[list the product description for the materials and equipment that were submitted, the specification section, and the date by which the response was due]*

  We notified you in our original submission and on [insert date] the dates by which a response was needed in order for us to avoid delaying our key work activities as follows:

  - *[list the product description for the materials and equipment that were submitted, and the key schedule activity that they impact]*

  This shall serve as our notice of delay in accordance with our contract [article #]. Since we are currently unable to release this material/equipment we will advise you of the impact to our schedule time and cost of performance as soon as we are able to determine the effect of this delay on our work.

  [1.2.3]

1.3 Requests for Information

Although the need to submit a Request for Information (or RFI) can arise at any point during a construction project, many RFI's typically originate during the period of time between the award of the contract and the contractor's mobilization for performance at the job site. This is because during this period of time a contractor is scrutinizing the contract documents, preparing submittals, ordering key materials and equipment, selecting the means and methods for performance, and making the detailed preparations for construction of the first phase of work.

You should be motivated to undertake as detailed a review of the plans and specifications as possible during the pre-construction and mobilization phase in order to bring to light as many potential conflicts and problems as you can. By doing so, you will gain the benefit of additional time with which to deal with the problems before they can have a serious impact on the work.

1.3.1 RFI to clarify drawings and/or specifications (clarification, missing information)

Keys:

- Prepare an RFI log and add each question or conflict to the log.
- Make sure to review the drawings and specifications carefully to avoid making unnecessary requests for information or clarification when the answers could be found in the Contract Documents.
- Consult the project schedule to identify the key work activities that are dependent on the response or clarification of the issue raised in the RFI.
- Note in the RFI log the date by which a response or clarification is required and set up calendar reminders for follow up.

> *Upon review of the Contract Documents [insert drawings, sections, elevations, specification or other details that locate the question] we have identified the following question[s] or conflict[s] that requires your response or clarification:*
>
> - *[list the question, problem or conflict that needs the attention or response by the design professionals]*
>
> *We believe that this question could be answered [or conflict could be resolved] by the following:*
>
> - *[describe a possible solution, if one has been identified]*

A response [clarification, or solution to the problem] is needed by [insert date] in order that we may be able to continue [or commence] with the work of [describe what work is affected by this issue]. Please contact us should you wish to discuss this request further. Thank you for your anticipated cooperation.
[1.3.1]

1.3.2 RFI response needed

Keys:

- Use reminder system set up in 1.3.1 to trigger the follow-up correspondence, ideally sent a few days before the response is needed.

  This is to inform you that we have not received a response to our RFI [insert #] which was sent to you on [insert date].

  We need to have a response or clarification by [insert date] in order to avoid a delay to our work according to the project schedule. *[1.3.2]*

1.3.3 RFI delayed, work impacted

Keys:

- Review the contract to obtain the notice requirements for delays.

  This is to inform you that we have not received a response to our RFI [insert #] which was sent to you on [insert date].

  We notified you in our original submission and on [insert date of follow-up notice] of the date by which a response was needed in order for us to avoid a delay to our [insert description of the key work activity or activities] resulting from the lack of response.

  This shall serve as our notice of delay in accordance with our contract [article #]. Since we are currently unable to start [or continue] this work we will advise you of the impact to our schedule time and cost of performance as soon as we are able to determine the effect of this delay on our work.   *[1.3.3]*

2. Performance

2.1 Revisions to Drawings and Specifications

2.1.1 New drawings issued

Keys:

- Whenever drawing (or specification) revisions are issued, it is good practice to notify the contractor (or the owner) how long you will need to review and compare the new documents with the existing ones to identify the changes and what the impact will be (if any) to the contract price and time.

    This will acknowledge receipt on [insert date] of the following Contract Documents:

    - *[insert list of documents – description, revision number, date]*

    We will need [insert time (days)] to compare these new documents with our existing Contract Documents in order to determine if there are any changes and to evaluate their impact on our contract price and time. [2.1.1]

2.1.2 Drawings and sketches given to field (not per contract)

There are times when in the haste of getting changes or additional information to the field, the design professionals manage to leave sketches, drawings or other details with field supervisory personnel. All field forces should be trained to alert the project manager of these situations so that the changes may be re-directed through the correct channels in accordance with the contract. It is critical not to start work on any unofficially distributed "change" until such time as that work is processed and is made a part of the contract.

Keys:

- Train all field project personnel to be aware that all changes to the Contract Documents of any type needs to originate from their project manager (or other administrative person with responsibility for the project).

   Please be advised that the following documents were given to our field supervision today by the [insert party who gave document]:

   - *[insert list of documents – description, revision number, date]*

   These documents were provided without going through the approved distribution method outlined in our contract. Consequently, we are ignoring these documents until you direct us otherwise.   *[2.1.2]*

2.2 Correcting the Record

2.2.1 Minutes of meetings

Keys:

- Review regularly the minutes of construction meetings.
- Clarify all mistaken entries in minutes of meetings that you attend and request in writing that they be corrected.
- Also ask to have the minutes reflect statements made which did not appear (for the record). Do this in writing.

   We have reviewed the minutes of construction meeting [insert # or date] and request corrections are made to the minutes as follows:

   - *[insert item number, description of corrected statement]*

   In addition, the following item was omitted from the minutes and we request that it be included:

   - *[insert item and statement omitted]*

   Please provide us with a copy of the revised minutes including the corrections noted above.   *[2.2.1]*

2.2.2 Correspondence with inaccurate statements

Keys:

- Clarify all mistaken entries and inaccurate statements that may appear in any type of correspondence (letters, emails, etc.) and do it in writing.
- Request that any derogatory or damaging statements be retracted.

> *We wish to correct your recent statement made in your correspondence [email, etc.] of [insert date]. Your statement about [insert inaccurate statement, quoted if necessary] is incorrect. The fact is [insert correction or explanation of why the statement was inaccurate].* [2.2.2]

2.3 *Materials & Workmanship*

General contractors are able to use the subcontractor meetings as a means of communicating their concerns on a regular basis about performance problems such as materials and workmanship that do not conform to the requirements of the contract. They are able to use the minutes of those meetings to record their oral communications. There may be times when this communication will be made separately, for emphasis or for compliance with specific contract notice requirements.

2.3.1 Materials not in conformance

> *The architect [or engineer] has informed us that you are installing materials on this project that do not conform to the requirements of the contract. The following materials do not meet the plans and specifications and were not approved for installation:*
>
> - *[insert a description of the material, the location installed, and specification section(s)]*
>
> *Be advised that in accordance with article [insert #] of the contract you are directed to remove this*

material and replace it with those that are approved for this project within [insert the time period specified in contract]. [2.3.1]

2.3.2 Workmanship not acceptable

<u>Keys:</u>

- Not all field installation problems will be evident in photographs. However, if appropriate, the use of photos that are well taken will be very effective in preserving a record of the condition that is unacceptable.

  The architect [or engineer] has informed us that your installation of [insert description of the work – include photos if the unacceptable work will be visible] does not conform to the standards of workmanship required by the contract.

  Be advised that in accordance with article [insert #] of the contract you are directed to correct or remove any unacceptable installed work to bring it to the required contract standard of workmanship within [insert the time period specified in contract]. [2.3.2]

2.4 Protection

General contractors are able to use the subcontractor meetings as a means of communicating their concerns on a regular basis about performance problems such as the need for subcontractors to protect their work from damage. They are able to use the minutes of those meetings to record their oral communications. There may be times when this communication will be made separately, for emphasis or for compliance with specific contract notice requirements.

2.4.1 Need to protect work

You are reminded that you are responsible for protecting your installed work in accordance with article [insert #] of the contract. This is necessary in order to prevent potential damage to your work from other work that remains to be completed in the area. We have not seen any protection for [insert description of the work and/or area] which has been completed by you.

Please install the needed protection within [insert time period] or we will be forced to do it for you and deduct the costs from your contract. Be advised that you will be responsible to repair or replace any work that is damaged as a result of your failure to protect the work. You will also be held responsible for any delay that results from such damaged work. [2.4.1]

2.4.2 Work damaged, not protected

You are hereby notified that the following work you installed was damaged as a result of your failure to protect the work as required by contract:

- *[insert description of the work and/or area damaged, include photos as appropriate]*

Please repair or replace the damaged work within [insert time period] as per article [insert #] of your contract. Please make sure to protect the work after you have completed the repairs or replacement to avoid future damage. [2.4.2]

2.5 Patching After Installed Work

General contractors are able to use the subcontractor meetings as a means of communicating their concerns on a regular basis about performance problems such as the failure to patch after installing work through walls or floors. They are also able to use the minutes of those meetings as their record of the oral communications. There may be times when this communication will be made separately, for emphasis or for compliance with specific contract notice requirements.

2.5.1 Patching not done

> *You are hereby notified that you are required to patch walls and floors/ceilings after installation of your work in accordance with the contract [insert article #]. The following areas need to be patched:*
>
> - *[insert description of the areas were patching is needed, include photos as appropriate]*
>
> *We need you to complete this work in order to be able to obtain inspection of the area. You are directed to complete this work within [insert time period] as per article [insert #] of your contract.*
>
> *[2.5.1]*

2.5.2 Patching to be done by others and back charged

> *We notified you on [insert date of first notice] of the need to patch the walls and/or floors in specific areas of the project after you installed your work (see our prior notice attached). Since you did not perform the necessary patching within the time required by the contract, we had the work performed on your behalf. Enclosed is a Change Order to deduct the cost of this work from your contract amount in accordance with article [insert #] of the contract.*   *[2.5.2]*

2.6 Cleaning-up

General contractors are able to use the subcontractor meetings as a means of communicating their concerns on a regular basis about performance problems such as the failure of subcontractors to clean up after performing their work. They are also able to use the minutes of those meetings as their record of the oral communications. There may be times when this communication will be made separately, for emphasis or for compliance with specific contract notice requirements.

2.6.1 Clean-up work not done

You are hereby notified that you are required to clean up after installation of your work on a daily basis in accordance with the contract [insert article #]. We have observed areas throughout the jobsite where clean-up has not been done.

- *[insert description of the areas were clean-up was not done, include photos as appropriate]*

This practice cannot continue. Be advised that you will be back charged for all future clean-up work which we undertake on your behalf in accordance with article [insert #] of the contract.   [2.6.1]

2.6.2 Clean-up work to be done by others and back charged

We notified you on [insert date of first notice] of the need to clean up after installation of your work (see our prior notice attached). Enclosed is a Change Order to deduct from your contract amount the cost of clean-up we were forced to perform this week [or other period] on your behalf, in accordance with article [insert #] of the contract.   [2.6.2]

2.7 *Rejection of Work*

<u>Keys:</u>

- When work is rejected by the design professionals the general contractor must take immediate action to make sure it is corrected in order to mitigate the impact to the project.

  The architect [or engineer] has informed us that your installation of [insert description of the work] has been rejected [include photos if appropriate].

  You are directed to correct or remove any installed work to bring it to the requirements of the contract in accordance with article [insert #] of the contract

within *[insert the time period specified in contract].
If you fail to correct this deficiency within the time
period noted it will be corrected by others and the
costs will be deducted from your contract by Change
Order in accordance with article [insert #].* [2.7]

2.8 Cure Period

2.8.1 Rejected work to be corrected

Keys:

- Subcontractors need to take notices of rejected work
  seriously and do everything possible to correct the work
  so that it will be acceptable and in accordance with the
  requirements of the contract.
- Subcontractors must be aware of the time allowed for
  correction and for response in these circumstances in
  order to keep the problem from escalating into a larger,
  more costly dispute.

  *We are in receipt of your notice informing us of the
  rejection of our work [describe the work rejected].
  We have started making the necessary corrections
  and anticipate being complete by [insert date]. We
  have brought in additional resources to make sure
  that other work on the project will not be affected.*

  [2.8.1]

2.9 Labor Force

2.9.1 Insufficient progress being made

General contractors are able to use the subcontractor
meetings as a means of communicating their concerns
on a regular basis about lack of progress on aspects of
the work. They are able to use the minutes of those
meetings to record their oral communications. There
may be times when this communication will be made
separately, for emphasis or for compliance with specific
contract notice requirements.

You are hereby notified that insufficient progress is being made by your company on the following activities in order to keep the pace required by the project schedule:

- *[insert a description of the activities, ID number]*

We are concerned that at your current pace of work you will be delaying the project schedule. We request that you review this work and make whatever adjustments are necessary to your resources in order to get the progress back on schedule. Should the pace continue to lag the schedule, we will be forced to supplement your work force and deduct the cost from your contract amount in accordance with article [insert #] of the contract. [2.9.1]

2.10 Supplementing Labor

2.10.1 Notice of intent to supplement labor

On [insert date] we notified you of the lack of progress being made in [insert description of work activities] and that your work was lagging the project schedule. This deficiency has continued and is now affecting the project schedule.

This shall serve as our notice in accordance with article [insert #] of the contract that we intend to supplement your labor force in order to improve the pace of this work and minimize the delay if you do not improve the pace of your performance by [insert date]. Should it become necessary for us to supplement your work, all costs incurred will be deducted from your contract amount by Change Order. [2.10.1]

3. Coordination & Sequence

3.1 Coordination of Work

The general contractor normally holds periodic project meetings for the purpose of coordination between the various subcontract trades. In order to minimize installation conflicts between the trades, it is essential that the key subcontractors actively participate in these meetings to anticipate and resolve potential conflicts before they surface on the project and become costly problems or delay the work.

3.1.1 Coordination of layout with other trades

Keys:

- General contractors must play an active role in supervising the subcontractor coordination meetings and in facilitating the prompt resolution of any conflicts that arise between subcontractors.
- The general contractor typically sets up a schedule for coordination and guides the subcontractors' efforts, setting ground rules to identify which subcontractor will take priority in the layout of his work in common spaces where the work of many subcontractors will be installed.

  As you know, your active participation at the weekly subcontractor coordination meetings is mandatory and required by contract [insert article from contract]. Your irregular attendance at these meetings has been noted in the past (see our correspondence of [insert date] attached).

  You are currently hindering the efforts of the other subcontractors who are attempting to complete the coordination of this phase of the project. You are directed to complete all of your layout work required for coordination by [insert date]. We will look to your company for any delays associated with your failure to participate in this coordination as required.   *[3.1.1]*

3.1.2 Failure to coordinate the work of other trades

A general contractor (or construction manager) that does not self-perform any of the work generally has certain duties by contract that is directly connected to the performance of the work by others for the benefit of the project. Key among them is the responsibility to 1) schedule the work, and 2) to coordinate the work of the subcontractors on the project.

General contractors who take a laissez-faire attitude towards their duties to schedule and coordinate the work of subcontractors do so at their own risk. These GC's may lose control over the work, and in the process lose the respect of the subcontractors and ultimately that of the owner as well. Their projects will tend to have more numerous and greater problems with subcontractor issues and the protracted nature of the problems will result in longer project delays.

Keys:

- General contractors need to practice proactive management. They have to coordinate the work of the subcontractors, anticipate problems and deal effectively with issues as soon as they arise.
- General contractors are well advised to track the progress of the work carefully and to take action whenever that progress begins to lag the schedule. This is especially the case for all activities that lie on the critical path.

  [from subcontractor] Our company has noted in various project meetings that you have failed to coordinate and manage the work of the subcontractors on this project (see meeting minutes [insert #'s] and correspondence dated [insert date]). This failure to coordinate the work has resulted in numerous unnecessary conflicts, disruption of work, re-sequencing and delays.

This "hands off approach" on your part which is forcing the subcontractors to attempt to sort out important issues on their own is unproductive, since there is no direct contractual relationship between the subcontractors. This approach has also created a free-for-all atmosphere on the project between the subcontractors, where work is performed without coordination, with little or no regard for the work of other trades. These conditions are having an adverse effect on productivity and increasing the cost of labor for our company.

This shall serve as our notice under article [insert #] of the contract of our intent to file a claim for the additional costs and time associated with your failure to coordinate the work on this project.

[3.1.2]

3.2 Materials Furnished by Others

Owners often decide to make direct purchases of materials and equipment and have them assigned to the contractors for installation. Many times this is done in order to get products with long lead times ordered before the project has been let out to bid. When you are responsible for furnishing the materials or equipment that are needed on the project, you must make sure that your product submittals are prepared in time to allow for approval, fabrication and delivery to the jobsite in time to meet your installation schedule. However, situations where the owner is furnishing materials can present additional sources of conflict for contractors who may have very little control over the order and may need to rely on others for information and details for delivery.

3.2.1 Materials furnished by others needed

Keys:

- It is critical to document as early as possible the dates when the materials furnished by others will be needed on the project for installation.

- It is also important to specify any special shipping, packaging and handling instructions that will facilitate receipt, storage, handling and installation of the materials or equipment furnished by others.

  This is to inform you of the dates that the following owner furnished materials and equipment will be required at the jobsite in order to meet the project schedule:

  - *[insert a description of the materials/equipment and the dates needed]*

  In addition, we have the following special instructions for packaging and delivery in order to facilitate our receipt and handling at the job site:

  - *[insert any special instructions]*

  We appreciate your cooperation. Please notify us if there are any problems complying with our instructions above. *[3.2.1]*

3.2.2 Materials furnished by others not suitable

We received the [insert description of material or equipment] at the project site on [insert date]. Unfortunately, this [material or equipment] was [damaged, incorrect, defective, etc.] and is not suitable for installation in the condition received. Enclosed are photographs showing the [damage, defect, etc.].

Please let us know what arrangements you make with the vendor for the [return or repairs] of this [material or equipment]. We will need to have suitable materials for installation by [insert date] in order to avoid delaying the project schedule. [3.2.2]

3.2.3 Delay in materials furnished by others

Keys:

- Make sure to comply with the timing in the notice provision of the contract for delays.

    This is to inform you that we have not yet received the [materials or equipment] from you at the project. In our prior correspondence of [insert date] (copy attached) we notified you that the materials were needed by [insert date] in order to meet the project schedule.

    This shall serve as our notice of delay in accordance with article [insert #] of the contract. We will submit our request for the additional time needed once the materials are received on the project.   [3.2.3]

3.3 Separate Contractors

Similar to the owner's direct purchase of materials, sometimes owners decide to contract independently for specialty work or finishes. Typically, the work of coordination with these separate contractors is left to the general contractor. Quite often, the separate contractor (or vendor) will not share the same spirit of cooperation as the contractors that are bound together with the general contractor by contract. This different attitude can also exist when the owner is paying the separate contractor directly, by-passing the general contractor. Consequently, there is the potential for additional sources of conflict on projects where the owner enters into separate contracts for portions of the work.

3.3.1 Work by separate contractors needs to be coordinated

Keys:

- It is especially important to be proactive and begin to coordinate with the owner and his separate contractors as soon as it is known that they will be involved in a project.

142

- Any lack of cooperation on the part of the separate contractors should be brought to the owner's attention immediately in order to avoid a bigger problem.

  [from Subcontractor to GC] As you know, our work of [insert description] has been dependent upon the progress of the work of the separate contractor hired by the owner. Despite our attempts to coordinate closely with their representative, they continue to show up sporadically and fail to work when planned. This has disrupted our work in this area. If this lack of coordination continues we will be unable to complete our work as planned. [3.3.1a]

  [from GC to Owner] We need to bring to your attention that [insert name of separate contractor] is not cooperating with the subcontractors on this project. Despite our best efforts to coordinate his work with the other subcontractor on this project to meet the demands of our schedule, he has failed to show up for work when required, and has refused to communicate with us when he is not going to show up. This conduct has disrupted the work of other subcontractors who are dependent upon his work. Attached is our correspondence to [name of separate contractor] and the correspondence from our subcontractor that is self-explanatory.

  We ask that you assist us to bringing this situation under control by attending a special meeting we have scheduled in order to avoid additional cost and delay to the project.   *[3.3.1b]*

3.4 Sequence of Work

3.4.1 Response to request to perform work out of sequence

Keys:

- It is necessary to keep a separate account of the cost to perform work that is affected by changed conditions (such as re-sequencing).

  You have directed us to proceed with the [describe the work] in [describe the area] of this project. As you know, there have been delays to the following activities on this project which were recorded in the recent minutes of our subcontractor meetings [or refer to other correspondence - insert reference]. It appears that these events will require significant re-sequencing of our work and unreasonably alter the planned, efficient execution of this work upon which our contract price was based.

  The re-sequencing of our work will lead to extensive come-back work in many areas which will increase our cost of performance. In addition, we anticipate that installing our work out of sequencing could result in an inordinate amount of damage to our work.

  This shall serve as our notice that we view your directive as a change in accordance with article [insert #] of the contract. We will quantify our added costs due to the changed circumstances under which we will be performing the work described above. Those costs will be compiled and submitted to you for reimbursement.   [3.4.1]

4. Payment

4.1 Progress Payments

The fundamental premise in every construction contract is the obligation of the contractor (or subcontractor) to perform and the obligation of the owner (or general contractor) to pay in exchange for that performance. This transfer of value takes place periodically in accordance with specific rules set forth in the contract. Therefore, being fundamental to the bargain, the obligation to pay should be strictly enforced by those that perform.

4.1.1 Progress payment delayed

Keys:

- You should treat the due dates for progress payments with the utmost importance, especially at the beginning of the project in order to avoid giving the impression that delayed payments are acceptable.

Caution:

- Consult with your attorney regarding any payment dispute.
- The contract may provide legitimate reasons for payments to be withheld (e.g. defective or non-conforming work that needs to be corrected).

> *[upon first delay of payment] This is to inform you that we have not received payment for our progress requisition [insert #] which was supposed to be paid on [insert date] in accordance with our contract.*
>
> *If there is any valid reason for withholding our progress payment please let us know so that we may be able to correct it. Otherwise, we expect to be paid on time to allow us to continue to perform as required on this project.* [4.1.1]

4.1.2 Non-payment

Keys:

- Work with your attorney to include language in your contracts that allows you to suspend performance on work that is not being paid (without a valid performance problem).

Caution:

- Consult with your attorney when negotiating your contract and when preparing correspondence regarding any payment dispute.
- The contract may provide legitimate reasons for payments to be withheld (e.g. defective or non-conforming work that needs to be corrected).
- The contract may also contain language that allows a contractor not to pay until payment is received by the owner. It may also require the continuation of work without payment.

    [assuming no valid contractual reasons for non-payment exist] Our company has not been paid its progress requisition [insert #] which was due on [insert date] in accordance with our contract. This shall serve as our notice of our intent to suspend performance on this project if payment is not received by [insert date]. [4.1.2]

4.2 Retainage

4.2.1 Request reduction in retainage

Keys:

- Work with your attorney to include language in your contracts that allows you to reduce your retainage at some point during performance in order to alleviate the cash flow on the project.

Caution:

- Consult with your attorney when negotiating your contract.

    We have satisfactorily completed [insert completion milestone for reduction in retainage from your contract] of our work on this project. In accordance with article [insert #] of the contract we request a reduction of our retainage for all progress requisitions from this point forward. [4.2.1]

5. Changes

5.1 Change Orders

5.1.1 Request for change order

Keys:

- Make sure to issue your requests for change orders timely.
- Prepare a change order log that includes each of the changes requested.
- Include all pertinent documents that will demonstrate the increases in quantities or scope of work.
- Include a clear explanation of the changes and how they result in increased cost and/or time.
- Make sure to price the work in accordance with any unit prices that are included by contract.
- Price the work fairly and be prepared to justify your cost basis.
- Review the status of work affected, the schedule and the anticipated stability of your costs to arrive at the time period through which you can extend your offer.
- Note in the change order log the date by which a response is required under the terms proposed and set up calendar reminders for follow up.

   We have priced the additional work contained in [insert document, drawing revision, etc.] issued on [insert date]. We are enclosing a copy of our estimate and a summary of the changes to our Scope of Work that result from this revision.

   Our price for this additional work is [insert price]. This additional scope will require an increase of [insert #] days to our contract time. We will not proceed with installation of this additional scope without written approval in accordance with our contract.

   Your prompt response is requested in order for us to adjust our work plan, procure materials and allocate the resources necessary to perform this additional work. We reserve the right to revise the price and time requested in this proposal if it is not approved within [insert #] days.   *[5.1.1]*

5.1.2 Follow-up request

Keys:

- Use the reminder system set up in 5.1.1 to trigger the follow-up correspondence, ideally to send a few days before the response is needed.

  This is to inform you that we have not received a response to our request for Change Order [insert #] which was sent to you on [insert date].

  We remind you that the terms of our proposal are only good through [insert date]. If our proposal is not accepted by that date we will be re-pricing it to take into consideration the current status of the work, any changes in our cost basis and the availability of resources to perform this additional work.   *[5.1.2]*

5.1.3 Approved changes requiring change orders

Keys:

- Use the change order log set up in 5.1.1 to send periodic reminder notices for all changes that have been approved but which have no Change Order issued.
- You should resist commencing any additional work without a Change Order to your contract or some specific means established for payment.

  We were notified on [insert date] that the following change order requests have been approved; however, we have not yet received a Change Order:

  - *[list the change order request #, description, date submitted, date C.O. required, amount requested]*

  Work has proceeded on these changes pursuant to your direction with the understanding that a Change

Order was soon to follow. However, to date no Change Orders have been received. It is unreasonable to expect us to continue to work on this additional scope without payment.

Be advised that unless we receive Change Orders for the above extra work by [insert date], we will be forced to suspend our work on the changes. We will look to your company for payment of all additional work performed and for the re-mobilization costs and delays that may result from the need to suspend performance on these changes. [5.1.3]

5.2 Change Directives

5.2.1 Directive to proceed with change pending agreement on price

You are directed to proceed with the work described in [insert description, change proposal #, RFI response, Bulletin #, Drawing Revision #, etc.]. We will issue a Change Order after the architect has completed his review of your proposal. [5.2.1]

5.2.2 Response to directive (with no agreement on price)

<u>Keys:</u>

- Make sure to get any direction to proceed with extra work in writing.
- Review your contract to understand what the options are for proceeding with extra work when there is no agreement on price.
- Don't proceed blindly based on a directive unless you are required to do so by contract.

<u>Caution:</u>

- Consult with your attorney regarding any work in dispute.

We received your Directive instructing us to proceed with the work of [insert description of the extra work]. In order for us to proceed with this extra work in accordance with the contract it necessary to select a method for proceeding as described in [insert article #, section #] of the contract.

Please advise us how we are to proceed based on the contract so that we will have a method of billing for this additional work as it performed. [5.2.2]

5.2.3 Directive to proceed with change (price: time & material)

You are directed to proceed with the work described in [insert description, change proposal #, RFI response, Bulletin #, Drawing Revision #, etc.]. You are to proceed on a time and material basis in accordance with [insert article #, section #] of the contract.

Please include all of the backup documents with each invoice in accordance with the contract and have all labor recorded on work tickets and submitted for signature daily. [5.2.3]

5.2.4 Directive to proceed with work (not a change)

Keys:

- Rejection of extra work requests should be made with a clear explanation provided that focuses on the reasons why the work is included within the original scope of the contract.

  Your request for change order [insert #] is rejected [by the Architect or Owner]. This work is not additional in scope for the following reason(s):

  - *[insert detailed support to justify why the requested extra work is included in the original scope under the contract – list plans, sections, details, notes, specifications, addenda, etc.]*

You are directed to proceed with this work without delay.   *[5.2.4]*

5.2.5 Proceeding with directed work under objection

There are four basic categories for extra work disputes:

1. There is no agreement that the work is additional in scope.
2. There is agreement that the work is additional in scope, but there is no agreement on the price.
3. There is agreement that the work is additional in scope, but there is no agreement on the additional time needed.
4. There is agreement that the work is additional in scope, but there is no agreement on the price or additional time needed.

The examples below will address each of these types of objections.

Keys:

- Research the contract documents and the facts to make sure your objection is sound before you go on record with it.
- When you are not on firm footing with your objection and you are forced to back-pedal, you will understandably lose credibility and your future requests will be subject to greater scrutiny.

Caution:

- Consult with your attorney regarding any work in dispute.

> *[objection: added scope] We received your Directive instructing us to proceed with the work of [insert description of the extra work]. Your Directive also informed us of the rejection of our change order request for this additional work. This is to inform you that we are proceeding with this work under*

protest, since we consider this work to be additional in scope to our contract.

Please consider this as our notice of dispute under the contract [insert article #]. We will submit our dispute for resolution in accordance with the procedure in the contract and look forward to your cooperation to facilitate a timely resolution. [5.2.5a]

[objection: price] We received your Directive instructing us to proceed with the work of [insert description of the extra work]. Your Directive states that the architect has approved this change for an amount that is lower than that which we requested. This is to inform you that we are proceeding with this work under protest, since we consider the fair value of this additional work to be as stated in our proposal.

Please consider this as our notice of dispute under the contract [insert article #]. We will submit our dispute for resolution in accordance with the procedure in the contract and look forward to your cooperation to facilitate a timely resolution. [5.2.5b]

[objection: additional time] We received your directive instructing us to proceed with the work of [insert description of the extra work]. Your directive states that the architect has approved our amount requested but not the additional time. This is to inform you that we are proceeding with this work under protest, since we consider our request for additional time to perform this change to be reasonable and justified as stated in our proposal.

Please consider this as our notice of dispute under the contract [insert article #]. We will submit our dispute for resolution in accordance with the procedure in the contract and look forward to your cooperation to facilitate a timely resolution. [5.2.5c]

[objection: price and additional time] We received your directive instructing us to proceed with the work of [insert description of the extra work]. Your directive states that the architect believes this is a change in our scope, but is not in agreement with the amount of our request or the additional time. This is to inform you that we are proceeding with this work under protest, since we consider our request for additional cost and time to perform this change to be reasonable and justified as stated in our proposal.

Please consider this as our notice of dispute under the contract [insert article #]. We will submit our dispute for resolution in accordance with the procedure in the contract and look forward to your cooperation to facilitate a timely resolution. [5.2.5d]

6. Schedules, Modifications & Delay

6.1 Progress Schedules

6.1.1 Request schedule update

Keys:

- It is important for contractors to track the progress of the work in the field and compare it to the current schedule that is in effect.
- Whenever significant deviations develop in key areas of the work, it may make the schedule ineffective for use to guide the work.
- If the schedule is not updated to reflect the actual progress of the work and to show the changes in sequencing, it may result in confusion, conflicts, and other problems on the job that could derail the project.

  We have recently noted that the work on the project does not appear to be tracking the project schedule. We brought this matter to your attention during the last weekly subcontractor meeting. The delays in some key activities and the out of sequence work are making it difficult for us to plan our work. We request that a revised schedule be issued so we may be able to plan and execute efficiently the remainder of our work. Please let us know if you would like our input to revise the schedule. [6.1.1]

6.1.2 Response to schedule update – compression of work

We received your recent schedule update of [insert date]. Our review of this update reveals that some of our work activities have been compressed from the original duration as follows:

- *[insert activity ID, description, original duration, revised duration]*

In order for us to complete those work activities within their compressed time frame, it will be necessary to accelerate our performance by increasing our workforce and/or by working overtime. Either of these changes will reduce our planned productivity for this work and will increase our cost of performance.

The changes to the project schedule were not the result of any failure to perform on the part of our company. Be advised that we consider the acceleration of our work to be a change to our contract. We will evaluate the impact and submit our request for Change Order in accordance with article [insert #] of our contract.   *[6.1.2]*

6.2 Delay

6.2.1 Notice of delay (general)

Keys:

- The subcontractor meetings provide a forum for communicating concerns on a regular basis about lack of progress on aspects of the work. General contractors are also able to use the minutes of those meetings as their record of the oral communications. Subcontractors must take care to verify that their comments during the meetings are reflected accurately in the meeting minutes.

- Although delays that are recorded in the minutes of subcontractor meetings help to prove that the contractor had knowledge of the delay, a subcontractor should still communicate all delays separately and comply with the specific notice requirement in the contract.

  The following work activities are currently lagging the project schedule and will delay the start of our work which follows:

  - *[insert activity ID, description of the activities, follow-on work delayed, planned start date, projected start date]*

Please consider this our notice of delay in accordance with article [insert #] of the contract. We will provide you with additional information concerning the extent of the delay as soon as we are able to determine the impact. [6.2.1]

6.2.2 Notice of delay (interference/disruption by others)

Our work of [insert description of the activity or work area being delayed] is being delayed due to the interference [disruption] caused by [insert the trade and/or describe the event that is causing the interference].

We have currently been delayed [insert #] days due to this interference [disruption] with our work.

We request your help in eliminating this interference [disruption] so that we may be able to proceed with the remainder of our work on [insert the activity] without additional delay. [6.2.2]

6.2.3 Notice of delay (obstruction or restricted access to work)

This is to inform you that we are experiencing delays to our work of [describe the work activities or areas affected] by the restriction [or obstruction] from [describe the circumstances causing the obstruction or restriction of access, include photos if applicable].

We have currently been delayed [insert #] days due to the restricted access to our work.

We request your help in removing this obstruction [or restriction] so that we may be able to proceed with the remainder of our work on [insert the activity] without additional delay. [6.2.3]

6.3 Extension of Time

6.3.1 Request for extension of time

<u>Keys:</u>

- Requests for extensions of contract time should be made as a part of the requests for changes whenever additional time is needed to perform extra work scope. For an example of how to make this type of request, see 5.1.1.
- Requests for extensions of contract time as a result of delays (unrelated to extra work scope) should be made in accordance with the contract provisions for making such requests.

> *In our previous correspondence of [insert date] (attached), we notified you of the delay to our activities as follows:*
>
> - *[insert activity ID, description of work delayed]*
>
> *We have now determined that this work was delayed [insert #] days. Since this work is on the critical path for completion of the project, we request an extension of [insert #] days to our contract time in accordance with article [insert #] of our contract.* [6.3.1]

6.4 Acceleration

<u>Keys:</u>

- Requests to accelerate the work are typically done after first giving a notice of delay to the party that is delaying the work.
- Contracts usually contain specific steps to follow when the work is delayed and it must be brought back on schedule.
- Since there are many ways that the work can be accelerated, the means and methods of the acceleration are usually left to the contractor to decide, however, the request of a recovery schedule is advised

in order to have a proposed plan against which the progress of acceleration can be measured.

6.4.1 Request to accelerate work

Your work on [describe activity] has failed to track the project schedule. We notified you on [insert date] that you were delaying the project and needed to increase the pace of your work.

You are hereby directed to accelerate your performance in accordance with article [insert #] of the contract. In addition, please submit your recovery plan within [insert # of hours or days] to show how you intend to bring your work back on schedule as required by the contract.

Your failure to comply with our request will be considered a breach of contract.   *[6.4.1]*

6.4.2 Response to request to accelerate work

[no dispute over delay] In response to your request to accelerate our work on [describe the activity], we are increasing our crew size [or working overtime to increase the hours of work] in order to increase the pace of the work to make up for the current delay. We will monitor closely the progress of the work and make additional adjustments as warranted. Enclosed please find our recovery schedule as requested which projects our work to be back on schedule by [insert the date].

We trust that our efforts will meet with your approval.   *[6.4.2a]*

[dispute over delay] In response to your request to accelerate our work on [describe the activity], we wish to remind you that the delay which has taken place is due to [prior work delay, interference or disruption] caused by others. We notified you of this

problem in our correspondence of [insert date] (attached). However, the problem has persisted and has prevented us from being able to work at a productive pace.

We have been reluctant to increase our crew size [or work overtime] in order to increase the pace of the work to mitigate the delay since this will add to our inefficiency, due to the ongoing disruption. However, we will comply with your directive, but will do so under protest, as we believe that we are entitled to additional compensation due to the interference [or disruption] caused by others.

We are increasing our crew size [or working overtime to increase the hours of work] in order to increase the pace of the work to make up for the current delay. We will keep track of our additional costs and submit them to you periodically with our request for reimbursement. Enclosed please find our recovery schedule as requested which projects our work to be back on schedule by [insert the date].

[6.4.2b]

7. Damages for Delay

7.1 Liquidated Damages

7.1.1 Notice of intent to assess liquidated damages

Caution:

- You should consult with your attorney when negotiating your contract and when preparing correspondence regarding critical issues such as liquidated damages.

  We have notified you in the past that your work has failed to keep pace with the project schedule (see correspondence attached). As a result, your company has contributed to the delays experienced on this project.

  This shall serve as our notice to you of our intent to assess liquidated damages in accordance with article [insert #] of the contract. We will deduct the liquidated damages from your final payment in accordance with article [insert #]. [7.1.1]

7.1.2 Dispute intent to assess liquidated damages

Keys:

- In order to be able to dispute liquidated damages caused by delay, it will help your position if you have documented the reasons why the delays alleged were not caused by you.
- If there is no documentation during the project to demonstrate the reasons for the delays, it will be much more difficult to defend against the assessment of liquidated damages for delay.

Caution:

- Consult with your attorney regarding disputes that involve liquidated damages.

  We received your notice of intent to assess liquidated damages. We dispute that we should be assessed any liquidated damages at all. In fact, we

161

have provided you with notices of delay throughout the course of this project which demonstrate that our company was not responsible for any of the delays. Below is a list of some of our key correspondence regarding delays which were sent to you in the past (copies attached):

- *[insert date, description of delay issue addressed in correspondence]*

In many of our communications we requested additional time for the delays that were experienced through no fault of our company. Our requests for additional time were not granted. On [insert date] we provided you with our notice of claim for our additional costs related to the delays on this project (see attached). We will be submitting our claim to you in accordance with our contract, once we have determined the added cost.   *[7.1.2]*

8. Claims

8.1 Notice of Claim

Most contracts require contractors to file a notice of claim when there is a dispute. In addition, some contracts will first require the contractor to file a notice of dispute. There are a variety of reasons why a contractor may need to provide a notice of claim (or dispute). The most common ones involve disagreements over the scope of the work (extras) and disagreements over delays in performance of the work. I have provided above a few examples of proposed language for extra work disputes in appendix 3.1.2 (failure to coordinate work of other trades); 5.2.5a (scope of work); 5.2.5b (price of extra work). I also included in the examples above some language for disputes that involve delays in appendix 3.4.1 (performing work out of sequence); 5.2.5c (time for extra work); 6.2.1 (general notice of delay).

Keys:

- The notice of claim should be straight forward, noting the subject of disagreement, including reference to prior correspondence concerning the disagreement, and citing the contract article that governs the submission of claims.

Caution:

- Consult with your attorney regarding any claims for disputes.

  Our company has disputed the [insert subject of the dispute] in prior correspondence to you dated [insert date] (copy attached).

  This shall serve as our notice of claim in accordance with article [insert #] of the contract.

  We will be submitting our claim for additional compensation [and/or time] as soon as we are able to determine the impact of the [describe issue in dispute] on our work.   [8.1]

9. Resolution of Claims & Disputes

The correspondence associated with the resolution of claims and disputes will necessarily be intricately tied with the language and procedures outlined in the contract. Usually, by the time that disputed construction issues reach the point where claims are submitted, the parties in the dispute have had the benefit of consultants and legal counsel in both preparing and corresponding about their claims.

The nature of construction disputes and the language in the contracts which govern them can be extremely varied so it is not possible to give examples that would be applicable to all conditions. You are strongly advised to seek the assistance of professionals to help you draft the documents that are needed in these situations.

10. General

10.1 Punch List

10.1.1 Objection to Punch List items – extra work

Keys:

- Punch lists often contain items that are really extra work. Contractors need to review the items on punch lists carefully and separate those items that are believed to be extra work prior to issuing the list to their field staff for completion.
- All items that are thought to be extra work should be submitted to the Architect (or general contractor) with an explanation of why it is considered to be extra work.

   We have received the Punch List dated [insert date] covering [insert the work or the area of the Punch List] and would like to call your attention to the following items in that list that we believe represent extra work to our contract for the reasons stated below:

   - *[insert item #, item description, reason issue is considered to be extra work]*

   We are proceeding to complete all of the other items on the Punch List with the exception of those identified above. Please let us know if you would like for us to submit a price for performing the additional work identified.   *[10.1.1]*

10.2 Inspection & Acceptance

10.2.1 Start of warranty period for equipment

Keys:

- The warranty period for equipment that is installed on a project is generally dictated by the contract. However, the start of the warranty period is often the subject of contention on projects where delays occur. Contractors are advised to negotiate the proper terms in their contracts so that they will not have to argue when the start of the warranty period takes place on projects that are delayed.

We received our final inspection and acceptance of the tests and installation of the major equipment on this project as follows:

- *[insert equipment description, date of testing, date of acceptance]*

Be advised that as this equipment has been placed in service, and accepted, the warranty period has started on [insert date], the date the equipment was accepted.   *[10.2.1]*

Acknowledgements

It's not possible to undertake a project such as this without the support, influence, comments and contribution of some special people who I would like to recognize. First, my dear wife, Nancy, who was very patient serving as my "test audience" during the rehearsals for the seminar series from which much of the material in this manual is based. She provided valuable feedback and was a positive force that motivated me to complete this book during the past year.

I also appreciate the effort of my brother, Julio, who willingly accepted the task of reviewing the manuscript and was kind to offer constructive suggestions and corrections to my work.

This book would not have been possible for me to write without the experiences obtained through the work that I have done for my clients and their lawyers since I began my consulting business in 1992. Although I have helped them, the insights I have gained through my work with them has taught me so much at the same time.

Finally, I give thanks to the Lord, Jesus Christ, my source of strength and inspiration, who makes everything possible.

CPSIA information can be obtained
at www.ICGtesting.com
Printed in the USA
FSHW01n1321020618
48733FS